To
- L.
I will always
remember our great
time together in the
Barrier Reef -
Love
Ann June-1980
Australia

S0-ATO-878

The Australian Great Barrier Reef in colour

K. GILLETT, FRPS, FRMS, AFIAP

REED

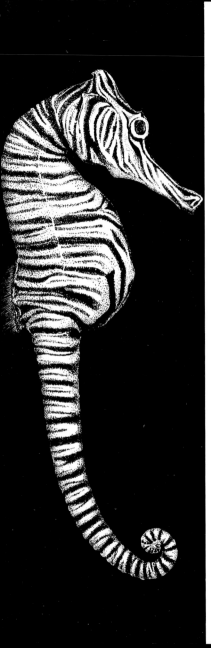

First published 1968
Reprinted 1971, 1976
This edition 1980

A. H. & A. W. REED PTY LTD
53 Myoora Road, Terrey Hills, Sydney
68-74 Kingsford-Smith Street, Wellington
11 Southampton Row, London
also at
Auckland and Christchurch

© Keith Gillett 1980
  All rights reserved. No part of this publication may be
  reproduced, stored in a retrieval system, or transmitted in any
  form or by any means electronic, mechanical, photocopying,
  recording or otherwise, without the prior written permission of
  the publishers.

National Library of Australia
Cataloguing-in-Publication data:
Gillett, Keith, 1929-
  The Australian Great Barrier Reef in colour.
  (Reed colourbook series)
  Index.
  ISBN 0 589 50199 2
  1. Great Barrier Reef. I. Title (Series)
919 43

Printed and bound by Kyodo-Shing Loong, Singapore

LEFT
The rare sea-horse *Hippocampus zebra*, drawn from an
actual specimen dredged from the Swain Reefs at a
depth of 38 fathoms (x1½).

contents

	page
Introduction	4
Coral reefs and their formation	6
True reef corals (Scleractinia)	14
Soft corals (Alcyonaria)	22
Branching corals (Gorgonacea)	26
Stinging corals (Hydrozoa)	28
Sea anemones (Actiniaria)	32
Worms (Vermes)	38
Great Barrier Reef shells (Mollusca)	44
Crabs and relations (Crustacea)	64
Echinoderms (Echinodermata)	70
Barrier Reef fishes (Pisces)	80
Marine turtles (Reptilia)	83
Sea-snakes (Reptilia)	88
Some birds of the Capricorn-Bunker Groups and Coral Sea	90
Index	94

introduction

NORTHWARDS from about Latitude 24° S., the north-eastern seaboard of Australia is protected from the Pacific Ocean swell by a natural breakwater. It extends for 1,250 miles to terminate in the waters of Torres Strait, at about Latitude 9½° S. Known as the Great Barrier Reef, this breakwater occupies an approximate area of 80,000 sq. miles and its distance from the mainland of the State of Queensland is anything from 7 to 42 miles.

This mighty offshore rampart is one of the wonders of the world – a great natural legacy rivalled only to a minor degree by another barrier reef of considerable size which occurs 800 nautical miles to the east of Queensland, off the coast of New Caledonia. This latter reef is approximately 400 miles long and rarely approaches closer than within 8 miles of the shore.

A full understanding of a vast and massive coral structure such as the Great Barrier Reef is in itself a deep and profound study. To think that, in the main, the constant industry of extremely small flowerlike forms of animal life could be responsible for the foundation work of such a structure is hard to believe. These are the countless millions of coral polyps, endowed with the capacity to build within the tissues of their soft flesh a great variety of hard but brittle skeletons of calcium carbonate. A detailed discussion on the form and function of these coral building polyps (true stony corals) is included in this book.

The Reef is not an unbroken coral-built wall as many might believe. It is a large collection of what could be termed reeferies, possibly likened to a coastline where outlets of rivers break the continuity of the land. Many channels or gaps do exactly the same thing with the Reef and in a few cases are wide enough for the passage of quite large vessels. Two navigable channels are Flinders Passage, east of Townsville, and Trinity Opening, north-east of Cairns.

The further the Reef is from the mainland, the more luxuriant and prolific are its coral growths. Inshore, these are retarded by the detrimental effect of sediments discharged from river mouths, particularly during floods. Similar conditions in the far north cause the abrupt ending of the Reef opposite the New Guinea Gulf of Papua.

Apart from comparatively recent discoveries, it is a matter of conjecture as to who were the first voyagers to blunder on the hazardous coral field of the Reef system. The Chinese have claimed that they possessed knowledge of the northern and eastern coasts of Australia more than 2,000 years ago. They were undoubtedly interested in exploring the seas to the south in search of the much prized sea-cucumbers or bêche-de-mer for drying and for the preparation of their famous soup. This industry was quite large in north-eastern Australian waters during the last century and in the early years after 1900, and has recently been revived in the far northern section of the Reef. History books used by students in Japan contain accounts of visits to the eastern Australian coast as far back as the fifteenth century. Either or both of the Chinese-Japanese claims may be authentic, but there is little evidence today convincing enough to substantiate them.

Both Spanish and Dutch explorers might well have approached the Reef from the east and have wrecked their vessels in the maze of coral patches of the Swain Reefs, east of Mackay, or at other points farther north. The writer visited the Swain Reefs in October 1960, on a charting expedition and observed quite a lot of wreckage from sailing ships of forgotten times on a number of small coral cays in the area. The Great Barrier Reef waters can be truthfully called one of the graveyards of the sea for they hold the secret of many unknown tragedies of the past.

Captain Matthew Flinders, whose surveys of the Australian coasts are part of Australia's historic past, was not spared the unenviable experience of being wrecked on a coral reef. In 1803 he joined the ship *Porpoise* for a passage from Sydney to England with charts he had compiled. The ship was lost beyond the Reef on the treacherous coral patches now known as Wreck Reefs (Latitude 22° 10′ S., Longitude 155° 28′ E.). Flinders' herculean task of organising a miniature colony for the survivors on a small sand cay, and the ultimate sailing of a cutter to Sydney for supplies, is one of the adventurous highlights of Australian history.

That prince of navigators, Captain James Cook, has been given the credit of being the first European to discover the Reef. In his 70-foot Bark *Endeavour* he sailed northwards along its entire length in 1770. He ran his ship aground on a coral reef close to Cape Tribulation, North Queensland. After emergency repairs, Cook succeeded in bringing the Bark *Endeavour* to the nearby mainland where it was beached and finally repaired in the mouth of a river he named after his ship. Cook jettisoned between 40 and 50 tons of ballast and other heavy equipment (including six cannon) in order to lighten the vessel. An American expedition located and salvaged four of the cannon in January, 1969.

Before the middle of the last century, the great Charles Darwin made a profound study of the origin and development of coral reefs. His world voyage on board HMS *Beagle* enabled him to study many and varied conditions at first hand, particularly those relating to the Great Barrier Reef. In recent years, valuable structural data has been obtained by the sinking of exploratory bores deep through the Reef mass at Michaelmas Cay, east of Cairns, and at Heron and Wreck Islands in the Capricorn Group, off Gladstone, Queensland.

It is hard to compare the Great Barrier Reef with much smaller reefs such as those in the Gulf of Mexico and off Bermuda, Ceylon, Fiji and Samoa. In this Great Barrier Reef system one can enjoy a stay on either of two coral island cays or at resorts snuggling among the hills of a number of the high or continental islands. These continental islands are a feature along hundreds of miles of the channel between the western margin of the Reef and the Queensland mainland – the above-sea-level fragments and peaks of an offshore mountain range rising from the submerged continental shelf.

The present publication is not intended to be a textbook on marine zoology or to compete with works which give more detailed coverage of the subject. It has been designed primarily to show the reader a few of the more outstanding animals which frequent coral reefs and briefly to detail their habits.

So great is the variety and form of the Reef fauna that one could spend a lifetime studying only a fraction of the animals which inhabit the area. The end result would be a mere whetting of one's appetite. No other ocean region in the world has been so lavishly endowed as this 1,250-mile strip of coral-built rampart and its adjacent waters. To view the beauty and colour of even a small bed of coral from beneath the water surface is a memorable experience.

CORAL REEFS AND THEIR FORMATION

CORAL REEFS can grow and flourish only in tropical seas, but certain non-reef-building kinds of coral do inhabit temperate, and even Arctic and Antarctic waters. In 1965 the French bathyscaph, *Archimède*, made a series of experimental dives in the Atlantic Madeira region off the Canary Islands, and photographs of corals were obtained at a depth of 7,550 ft. A beautiful little cup coral, *Carophyllia*, is a common inhabitant of waters off the English coasts, and appears to thrive in that area. Other corals of similar delicate structure also exist in offshore waters along the south-eastern and southern Australian coasts but are normally of a solitary type.

For the creation of massive coral reefs, such as those off the north-eastern Australian coastline and along the coastline of New Caledonia, certain conditions must prevail. Probably the most important factor is water temperature: it must not fall below 20°C. A continued absence of sediments is also vital, for these can smother a formation during its early development. The true reef-building corals do not normally occur below a depth of about 25 fathoms for, below this level, almost all sunlight essential to their multiplication and survival is absorbed. The microscopic plant cells (Zooxanthellae) that live in the fleshy tissues of corals are necessary for their development. These in turn need sunlight in sufficient strength for maintaining their own growth and development (photosynthesis). A great deal of research has been carried out on the function of these special minute plant cells, and it has now been proved that the reef-building corals derive benefits from them which they cannot do without.

The cells are essential to the chemical action needed for the skeleton of the coral to form.

While the calcareous skeletons of the corals are primarily responsible for reef-building, the ultimate consolidating process comes from other sources. Of first importance in this process are the stony seaweeds or nullipores (*Lithothamnion*) – growths embodying calcium carbonate extracted from the sea-water. Their spreading encrustations (usually mauve or purple in colour) tend in places to form a carpet over a coral bank, particularly along a margin subjected to the surge of ocean waves. It is thus that a binding or partial cementing action is effected. The final cementing into a hard limestone mass or platform at the surface of a coral bank comes from the clogging of any spaces, cracks and crevices with often powder-fine detritus sands, which are the dead waste products of any coral region and to a large

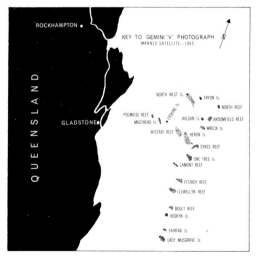

Colour photograph taken from *Gemini V*, manned satellite, 1965, by courtesy of National Aeronautics and Space Administration, USA, showing Capricorn-Bunker Groups from an altitude of 171.107 miles. Latitude 23.358 degrees South, Longitude 153.653 degrees East.

degree contain the remains of simple lime-secreting organisms called forams (Foraminifera). These forams unite with broken and dying coral growths and other large fragments of reef débris to bring about the final consolidation.

If all the coral reefs were recorded on a map of the world it would be quite apparent that they flourish mainly along the eastern shores of continents where the warmer sea currents prevail. The outstanding exception to this rule is the Abrolhos group of islands which are of coral origin and are situated off the West Australian coast in Latitude 29° S. It is true that in certain areas of the tropical seas there is an entire absence of coral reefs, and this presents some puzzling problems. A theory once propounded was that the proximity of volcanic land to areas of coral reefs greatly assisted the growths through the added seepage of lime into the sea. Today there are very few students who adhere to this view. Off the north-eastern coastline of Australia the water temperature and salinity are ideal and consequently coral polyps live and multiply. Conditions are so perfect that not only does the Great Barrier Reef exist but another type of reef also is to be found in these waters close to the mainland. This is called a fringing reef, and constitutes one of the three types which are to be found throughout the world, the other two being barrier reefs and atolls. But first a little should be said about this first type – the fringing reef.

Some better-known examples are to be found off Lindeman, Brampton, Dunk, Long, Hayman, and South Molle Islands, all of them comparatively close to the mainland. Strictly speaking, these fringing reefs form part of the Great Barrier Reef system. Their fauna is very closely related to that of the Reef proper farther to seaward and the many varieties of coral growths in the two areas are similar, especially the often large and spectacular Meandrine or Brain Corals, which may reach massive proportions in these ideal surroundings.

In his classic volume, *Coral Reefs*, Charles Darwin states that a fringing reef, sometimes referred to as a shore reef, is one skirting an island or part of a continent with the absence of any noticeable enclosed deep water channel. In other words, a fringing reef actually clings to and grows outwards from a shoreline.

Unlike a fringing reef, a barrier reef runs parallel to the coastlines of islands or continents, often standing off a considerable distance from them. The enclosed channel behind the barrier can be quite deep, as seen in the case of the Great Barrier Reef, where depths as great as 30 fathoms are common. Another feature of a barrier reef is its thickness. Some idea of this can be gauged from the results of an exploratory bore sunk through the coral cay known as Wreck Island, in the southern part of the Reef. This bore penetrated to about 1,800 ft. before underlying volcanic rock was encountered.

The third and most intriguing type of coral reef is the atoll, probably best described in the vivid words left to us by Charles Darwin. In 1843, while travelling westward across the Pacific on board *HMS Beagle*, he noted that "We saw several of the most curious rings of coral land just rising above the water's edge, which have been called Lagoon Islands. These low coral islands bear no proportion to the vast ocean out of which they abruptly rise; and it seems wonderful that such weak invaders are not overwhelmed by the all-powerful never-tiring waves of the great area, miscalled the Pacific."

Heron Island, showing a section of its extensive coral reef.

The atoll is the coral-type island of so many romantic associations in story and fiction – a central lagoon ringed by coral-built land. To view such a reef formation from the air is an enthralling experience. Inside the bordering of brilliant green foliage lie the placid turquoise waters of the lagoon, studded with coral beds of remarkable beauty and patterning. Unlike the waters surrounding either fringing or barrier reefs, the sea beyond the edge of an atoll plunges to great depths, sometimes running into thousands of fathoms. The world's classical atoll, and also the largest, is situated in the north-eastern quarter of the Indian Ocean. It is named Cocos-Keeling, has a long axis of 10 miles, and is more than 600 miles from land. In 1962 the writer was a member of an expedition which visited the virtually unexplored Chesterfield Reefs some 600 miles north-east of Port Curtis, Queensland. These oceanic coral-built formations (Latitude 19° 58′ S., Longitude 158° 28′ E.), enclose a central lagoon area and are most atoll-like in appearance. They seemingly spring from a bottomless ocean, and present a picture of amazing beauty and contrast. However, upon contemplation, one became quickly conscious of the dangers awaiting an unwary visitor to the region.

On the question of the origin and development of the three types of coral reefs, that of the fringing reef is the simplest and most easily understood. Corals soon establish themselves in the shallow water which is to be found near the shoreline of islands or continents, and soon grow upwards until they reach the surface. But regarding the barrier reef and its formation there is still no single explanation that can be generally applied. Scientists have concluded that every such reef is an individual formation, the product of varied factors, and is understandable only from its own special history. The origin of the atoll, sometimes thousands of miles away from major land-masses and arising from great ocean depths, is most confusing. Darwin's theory of reef formation is the answer which is upheld to this day by many scientists. His supposition was that the fringing reef came first, edging the slopes of a newly-formed island. As the island subsided, the corals, ever building on the same foundations, became divorced from the shore and their structure then assumed the form of a barrier reef. Finally the island disappeared completely, leaving a more or less circular coral-enclosed lagoon (an atoll).

Now that these three types of reefs have been described, attention can be centred on the coral cays or pseudo-atolls of the linked Capricorn-Bunker Groups – richly vegetated gems located 30 and more miles from the mainland. The groups comprise 15 small isles, interspersed with numerous coral banks and shoals. When tidal waters recede, the coral banks on which these picturesque little isles rest are exposed to reveal great expanses of coral platforms. To approach a coral cay from the sea is an experience in itself, for these islets seem to "pop up" out of a turquoise ocean above which they appear to be suspended. A fortunate feature of the Capricorn-Bunker Groups is that the coral banks become exposed when tide waters fall. This enables the visitor to walk out from the shore of any islet and view in comfort and safety the tremendous range of fauna which occurs on the coral banks.

In the Swain Reefs, lying a little farther to the north, the coral banks seldom completely uncover, even during the very low spring tides. This same condition is prevalent at other reef areas

Typical fringing reefs, Cumberland Group.

also known to the writer, but situated well out in the Coral Sea; these are the Chesterfields, Wreck, Kenn, Saumarez, Frederick Reef, and Cato Island. Even in the still wider Pacific areas such as the Fiji Islands and Western Samoa, up to 12 in. of water may still cover the main reef flats during the lowest of tides. These facts about variable tidal range are not generally known, and in comparing in particular the two opposite Reef examples, the explanation appears obscure. One tends to think that the answer might be that the Capricorn-Bunker assemblage of coral banks is of greater antiquity and hence greater in height than those comprising the Swain Reefs.

Heron Island, in the Capricorn Group, is one of a fairly tight cluster of cays. Nearby are the cays and coral banks of Wilson Island, North West Island and One Tree Island, and all offer virgin territory for exploration and research. As with all coral reefs, the region immediately below water level on the outer edge of a coral bank is the area where the most attractive coral growths are located. An inspection through crystal-clear water on a calm, sunny day can be truly awe-inspiring. The delicate structural beauty and colouring of the growths are enhanced by their submergence and, darting among the branches, the multi-hued fish population appears to be suspended in air.

Towards the northern end of the Reef there is one combination of islet, cay, and coral bank, to which scientists have given enduring fame. Low Isles is located about eight miles east of Port Douglas and is somewhat isolated from the western edge of the main Reef. History records that Captain James Cook was the first European to observe Low Isles. This was on 10 June 1770 when, on board *Endeavour*, he recorded in his log the passing of "a small low island which was about 2 Leagues from the Main; it being about high water". Another 158 years were to pass before a very real and lasting interest was to become centred on Low Isles. It was selected as headquarters of the now scientifically renowned British Great Barrier Reef Expedition, sponsored by the British Museum of Natural History.

In the years to come greater and far more rewarding knowledge of the sea will be gained by mankind. It will ultimately provide a much increased means of sustenance and certainly great wealth. Over the last 50 years the accelerated interest in the Great Barrier Reef alone has shown the potential of the region in mineral and oil deposits. But at this point, however, a timely and very essential note of warning must be sounded: it is that rigid controls should protect this natural wonderland from any form of widespread despoliation. Australia possesses one of the most complex and magnificent of Nature's legacies. Countless thousands of years have been necessary for its formation and growth, and to allow any form of destruction to follow in the name of "progress" would be a national crime.

Partially exposed reef flat, Heron Island.

TRUE REEF CORALS
(Scleractinia)

IN THE THIRD CENTURY A.D., Sextus Empiricus (Greek physician and philosopher) became interested in living corals and referred to them as "zoophytes", meaning an animal more or less resembling a plant in appearance and character. One thousand years later many naturalists and scientists believed they were plants and some even used the ludicrous term "coral insects" to describe them. It was in 1744 that the Frenchman Jean André Peysonnel, after observing living corals along the coast of North Africa, discovered that this flowerlike organism was actually a voracious carnivore. In fact, it was a type of simple animal life, a sea anemone, but with the added power of forming a limy skeleton. Unfortunately, his discovery was ridiculed at the time and it was left to a fellow-countryman, Réaumur, to give the name of "polyp" to the living animal. This term is still used to classify this form of marine life.

For the more seriously-minded naturalist or student of zoology, corals are a subdivision of the phylum, Coelenterata, or, as it is sometimes called, the Cnidaria by zoologists. Other members are hydras, jellyfishes, and sea anemones. The coral polyps' spectacular beauty is rivalled only by that of the sea anemones, for the fleshy animals of both groups are very similar in appearance when viewed alive.

There are more than 350 species of coral to be found on the Great Barrier Reef and although they are a rather difficult group to elaborate on, a little should be said about the true stony reef-building kinds which play a major role in the formation of the Reef. These busy architects are grouped by the zoologist and referred to as the Scleractinia. It would be beyond the scope of this book to describe the different patterns and the infinite beauty of the skeletons of all Reef corals, for when the fleshy animal dies, white bleached masses of calcium carbonate remain and in some cases rival the beauty of the living corals. Skeletal patterns resembling the human brain (Brain Corals) and others taking the shape of antlers (Staghorn Coral) are to be found in profusion on the Reef. Although they may vary quite considerably, the animal which is responsible for these diverse forms is essentially the same.

The polyp could be described as a small cylindrical sack of fleshy composition, having at the top a group of tentacles which can be retracted quickly if the animal is disturbed. These tentacles are essentially the same as those possessed by sea anemones and are used for defence and as a means of trapping minute living organisms. (This point will be further explained later.) Polyps vary a great deal in size. Some are only about 1 mm. in diameter, *Acropora*, and in the case of the true stony coral, *Goniopora tenuidens*, may attain a diameter of approximately 8 mm. One easy method of classification for this present group, Scleractinia, is that the tentacles always occur in multiples of six. This is an important item, for a little later on other types will be discussed and these latter species are often confused with the true reef-builders, which are quite different in many ways.

Feeding usually takes place at night, the corals employing the same method of obtaining food as the sea anemones. The prey is passed down to the mouth by the tentacles of the polyp or by water currents set up by countless numbers of fine hairs which occur on the surface of the tentacles of

Brain Coral, *Platygyra lamellina*.

some types. It is then passed on down the throat (stomodaeum) of the polyp to what is known as the coelenteron or digestive cavity. Extraneous material is removed by special flagellated currents. A visitor to the Reef may be a little disappointed on viewing living corals for the first time. True stony corals very seldom expand their polyps during the day and except in a few very rare cases (*Goniopora*), are night feeders, feeding on plankton which is more active during this period.

A little should be said about how corals reproduce and become established. In this one instance only, they can be compared with plants, for once they become established they are capable of spreading out over great areas, by releasing minute larvae called planulae. These resemble a pear in shape, measure about 1 mm. in length, and are generally covered in fine hairs (cilia). The mouth is at the broad end. The hairs act as miniature oars and move at great speed; in fact they are a means of locomotion for these planulae and keep them near the surface of the water. Great numbers are released by the polyps but only a small percentage survive, settle, and become attached, mouth uppermost, to some appropriate hard support. They soon undergo a complete metamorphosis; their base becomes flattened, and each appears like a little dome with the mouth at the top. Lime is soon produced at the bottom and if the polyp was examined under a microscope at this point a skeletal pattern would be apparent through the semi-transparent tissue. In a remarkably short time, six small knobs appear at regular intervals on the top of the juvenile polyp and these in turn develop into tentacles. Simultaneously with the appearance of these tentacles the edges of the internal partitions, or mesenteries, may be observed through the transparent body wall. In a short space of time an adult polyp is formed.

As stated earlier, the true stony corals or reef-builders flourish only in shallow water and at temperatures not below 20°C. The most common species to be found on the Reef is the staghorn type, *Acropora*, and it is probably one of the most spectacular of all Reef corals. Numerous colour variations are to be found ranging from pink and yellow to even a bright mauve. Sheltered water is a governing factor for *Acropora*, and growths can attain a height of more than six ft. in sheltered lagoons, such as Fitzroy Reef in the Capricorn Group. Heavy surf has a detrimental effect on this particular coral.

As a true reef-builder, the Meandrine or Brain Coral rules supreme. Easily identified by its shape and patterning, it can reach quite massive proportions. Smaller colonies of another common type are found on exposed coral reefs. This coral, *Pocillopora*, can be easily recognised by its delicate form and rose-pink or brownish colour. Yet another very important coral in reef formation is the species which appears as platforms of round flat-topped colonies and occurs profusely in the Capricorn-Bunker Groups. The polyps in this particular kind, *Porites*, are minute and even when expanded at night, are barely visible to human eyes. For beauty of sculpture and exquisite detail, the coral *Acrhelia horrescens* is a perfect example of Nature's handiwork. Unfortunately it is not a common one, though it is sometimes revealed at low spring tides. Another type (*Montipora*) which appears as graceful rosettes can be yellow, brownish-pink, green, or brown in colour and prefers sheltered coral pools. These are only a few of the many true stony corals which inhabit the Great Barrier Reef system.

Polyps of the true coral, *Goniopora tenuidens* (x7).

A specific type which resembles a mushroom in shape and has an extremely large polyp deserves an explanation. These are. the mushroom corals and the zoologist refers to them as fungids. There are two which are common to the Great Barrier Reef, the first being a coral, *Fungia fungites*, which the author has never yet seen with its polyp fully expanded during the day. It ranges in size from about 15 mm. to approximately 7 ins. in diameter and any Reef flat is virtually strewn with this species. When mature they are never attached in any way and can be handled and examined very easily. Their life history is very interesting, for the coral reproduces planulae in the normal way but the minute corals are actually fastened by a type of stalk, like a mushroom. They attach themselves to fragments of dead coral and when they attain a certain age they simply drop off. Where they settle is greatly governed by water movement but they usually prefer shallow water and are very rarely seen in the channels off the reef flats. Each coral possesses only one polyp which has an extremely large mouth. The tentacles are short.

Another, closely related, type occurs particularly in the Capricorn Group and in contrast to the previous coral is nearly always expanded during the day. This coral is *Fungia actiniformis*, and has large brownish-coloured tentacles. It is particularly prevalent at Broomfield Reef and One Tree Island. Some specimens may measure 6 ins. or more in diameter and this coral again has one large single polyp. There are other types of fungids to be found on the Reef, and one, *Herpolitha limax*, is usually found at depths of about 6 fathoms. It is commonly known as a Slipper Coral and grows to more than 12 ins. in length. In this coral, more than one polyp is

accommodated, and a series of mouths run down the centre of the large disc. Another close relation is *Polyphyllia*, one of the largest of the fungid group.

How long does coral live and how fast does it grow? There are certain corals at Bermuda which are known by tradition to have been living for centuries. A living reef just off Tahiti has remained at the same depth (about 3 fathoms) for nearly 100 years. Corals are invariably slow growers and to form an extensive barrier reef such as the one off the Australian coastline would take many hundreds of thousands of years.

Their rate of growth is another very interesting challenge to scientists. An early clue came in 1830, when a scientist made some experiments with corals on the east coast of Madagascar. He stated in his account: "To ascertain the rise and progress of the coral-building family, and fix the number of species met with at Foul Point (Latitude 17° 40′) twenty species of coral were taken off the reef and planted apart on a sandbank *three feet deep at low water*. Each portion weighed ten pounds, and was kept in its place by stakes. Similar quantities were placed in a clump and secured as the rest. This was done in December, 1830. In July following, each detached mass was nearly level with the sea at low water, quite immovable, and several feet long, stretching as the parent reef, with the coast current from north to south. The masses accumulated in a clump were found equally increased, but some of the species in such unequal ratios, as to be growing over each other." There is no record of what corals were planted on the sandbank, for the collection was lost in a shipwreck. Also, the level of the sea could have been different and probably was, at the two stated times, but it was apparent

Staghorn Coral, *Acropora humilis*.

through this experiment that certain corals do grow at different rates. There is another record of a ship's copper bottom being covered with an encrusting 2-ft. layer of coral growth in the Persian Gulf. It was not stated which corals were responsible for this remarkable growth and other forms of marine growth must have contributed to this thick layer over 20 months.

It was most fortunate that Saville Kent in 1890 measured the diameter of certain corals at a point near Thursday Island. Twenty-three years later, Dr A. G. Mayer measured these corals again and found that one species, a brain coral, had increased in diameter from 30 ins. to 74 ins., an annual increase of 1.88 ins. Another true reef-building type, *Porites*, which had a width of 19 ft. when measured by Saville Kent had increased during the same period to 22 ft. an annual increase of 1.95 ins.

Before the next group of corals is dealt with, mention should be made of some of the marine life associated with these corals. A coral reef is actually an association of many thousands of marine animals and just a few of these intimate relationships will be discussed. It is not unusual when viewing a living coral growth to see, as if by magic, beautiful petal-like structures emerge from their calcium carbonate dwelling places, then just as quickly disappear from view. Many people conclude that they are living coral polyps because of their flowerlike appearance. But these are the breathing gills of the marine worm, *Spirobranchus giganteus*, which makes its home in the skeletons of the corals. These worms possess remarkable colouring – light orange, pink, mauve, vivid blue, green, and even black variations are encountered.

On the outer edge of a reef, large clumps of dead coral will always be found and in some cases these jagged formations will still be seen protruding through the surface at high water. They are known as "niggerheads" and constitute a danger to seamen in these waters. Living in close association with them are to be found oysters, barnacles, and the common large chiton, *Acanthozostera gemmata*. The Reef oyster is a little stronger in taste than the ones which occur in southern waters.

Small clumps of dead coral are scattered everywhere along any coral reef. Although at first sight they appear uninteresting, they will generally reveal a teeming mass of marine fauna when turned over. In striking contrast to the dead brownish upper surface of the boulder, the underside in nearly every case will show an assemblage of colour. Bryozoans, egg masses of molluscs, sponges, ascidians and algae are a few which make their home beneath these boulders away from predators. It is most important that these dead clumps of coral be returned to their original position, for the marine life associated with the underside soon dies if exposed to the sun for any length of time.

Mushroom Coral, *Fungia actiniformis,* expanded by day, One Tree Island.

SOFT CORALS
(Alcyonaria)

As STATED EARLIER, and at the risk of repetition, corals are a most confusing group to explain. It is difficult to comprehend that this coelenterate can be "soft", and even more confusing when it is classified as a "false coral". Many people naturally assume that all Great Barrier Reef corals are hard, brittle, and beautifully sculptured growths of calcium carbonate. This is not so, for other kinds do exist and prosper on the Reef system and warrant a little explanation in this book.

The name Alcyonaria is applied to polyp-bearing animals which have eight pinnate or fringed tentacles. These are of a feathery appearance and immediately identify this group. They are commonly known as "soft corals". Barring a few exceptions, which will be dealt with in this section, all are of a flexible, almost leathery composition, a perfect example being *Sarcophyton trocheliophorum*, which is essentially a shallow-water dweller and an outstanding member of Reef fauna. In complete contrast to the nocturnal feeding habits of the true stony corals, it is not uncommon to see *Sarcophyton* feeding during the day with its thousands of pinnate-tentacled polyps fully expanded in search of minute living organisms. Colour variations occur with this species, ranging from greyish-blue, brown, and light green to a vivid bottle-green. It prefers small isolated coral pools and grows to quite large dimensions (about 4 ft. in diameter). The alcyonarians are a much hardier group than the true stony corals and do not seem to be unduly affected by silt or an excess of fresh water brought out by mainland rivers. Massive colonies are to be found on the fringing reefs which, as explained earlier, lie close to the Queensland coast to the north. Water temperature also does not seem to have much effect on them for certain species exist in Arctic waters and one, commonly known as dead-men's-fingers, is to be found off the English coast.

Other Reef types prefer much deeper water and are to be found at about the 20-fathom mark. They are a very intriguing group, for in many cases they are prickly to touch and feel as if thousands of needles are protruding from the flesh of the animal. Brilliant colours occur in the deeper water species but unfortunately these alcyonarians decompose very quickly when brought to the surface.

Possibly the most striking of all "soft corals" is *Xenia elongata*, easily recognised by its delicate appearance. It is very common and is to be found on all coral reefs. The colour of the polyps varies from a grey to greenish-blue and even a vivid pastel-blue. This species prefers shallow water.

Other alcyonarians are *Lobophyton* and *Sinularia*, which are both leathery to touch and are more prolific on the northern part of the Reef. Extensive colonies are found in the Cumberland Group of islands with their associated fringing reefs. The large Egg Cowry, *Ovula ovum*, is sometimes found associated with *Sinularia*. It apparently derives some benefit from this particular alcyonarian and it is a most remarkable sight to see this large mollusc, with its jet-black mantle fully extended, crawling over or seeking shelter in amongst the brownish fleshy folds of *Sinularia*. Although all the above soft corals do not possess a calcium carbonate skeleton they do have embedded in their tissues countless thousands of microscopic calcareous spicules of various shapes

Soft Coral, *Sarcophyton trocheliophorum*.

Skeleton of Organ-pipe Coral (x4).

and sizes. With the death of the polyps these spicules then play a very minor role in reef formation and consolidation.

There are two exceptions with this group, Alcyonaria, which do possess a type of skeleton, the first exception being the well known and easily identified Organ-pipe Coral, *Tubipora musica*. Along the shoreline of any coral cay will always be found small pieces of bright crimson-red coral resembling the pipes of an organ. These skeletons, unlike those of the stony corals, do not bleach white when exposed to the sun but retain their colour indefinitely. The parallel organ-pipe tubes, in which the polyps are accommodated, consist of fused spicules. To view the living coral is another matter, for the polyps are bright green and quite large (about 10 mm. in diameter). They completely cover and camouflage the crimson-red skeleton. *Tubipora* is an important constituent of a coral reef and occurs along the entire length of the Reef proper, as well as along mainland fringing reefs.

The second soft coral with a skeleton is the Blue Coral, *Heliopora coerulea*, which is restricted to the northern section of the Reef, occurring abundantly in the Torres Strait. This coral in its natural habitat on a reef is a dull bluish-grey but when the skeleton is fractured the internal colour is bright indigo-blue and, as in the case of *Tubipora*, it permanently retains its colour. Unfortunately, very little is known about this particular species mainly because it occurs in far northern waters and in areas which are usually inaccessible. In 1889, Saville Kent obtained live specimens of *Heliopora* in the neighbourhood of Warrier Island, Torres Strait, and although they were closely observed day and night in constantly renewed sea-water, the polyps refused to expand.

Soft Coral, *Xenia elongata.*

BRANCHING CORALS
(Gorgonacea)

THE MOST OSTENTATIOUS of the group now being discussed (Alcyonaria) are the branching corals, which are nearly always found in deeper water along the length of the Reef system. These elegant formations may be likened to plant life, for their fernlike structure resembles and rivals that of quite a few members of Australian flora for sheer beauty and intricate pattern. A typical example is the delicate Gorgonid Coral, *Mopsella ellisi*, which prefers deeper water. Its growths have a

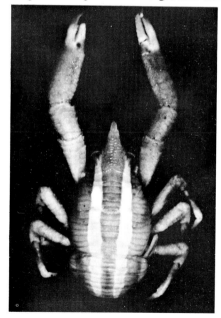

Krill-shrimp, *Galathea elegans* (x3).

tremendous range of colours – deep wine-red flecked with yellow, pink, mauve, yellow, and brown. When brought to the surface it retains its colour indefinitely, so different from the stony corals, which soon become bleached white calcium carbonate skeletons when removed from their natural habitat.

Gorgonid corals are particularly prevalent in the waters adjoining the Capricorn-Bunker Groups and even occur off the New South Wales coastline. To view a beautifully coloured branching growth of this species under water can be a remarkable experience for the skindiver. At depths of about 20 fathoms, where all forms of plant and animal life take on an eerie greenish appearance, the scene changes dramatically with the ignition of a flash-bulb, and *Mopsella ellisi* stands out as a colourful mass of detail.

The polyp of this group is very small indeed, measuring from about $1\frac{1}{2}$ mm. in diameter. It varies greatly in colour. Under magnification the pinnate tentacles can be seen clearly. Spicules are present in the brittle skeleton, which consists of horny axial rods. These branching growths are placed in an order called Gorgonacea and this includes sea-whips, sea-feathers and sea-fans, the latter being another name for the type now being discussed.

It is with this particular coral that one of the strangest relationships of all exists. When a growth is first viewed, nothing unusual will be noticed; but on a closer examination, it is not unusual to see small shells clinging to the framework of the coral. These exquisite little molluscs are cowry shells in miniature and possess an animal (mantle) with exactly the same colour as the growth. Small crustaceans (Plate 15) are also associated with this coral.

Gorgonid Coral, *Mopsella ellisi* (x8).

STINGING CORALS
(Hydrozoa)

IT HAS ALREADY BEEN EXPLAINED that the coral polyp is a voracious carnivore and depends on catching minute living organisms as a means of survival. How this tiny relation to a sea anemone accomplishes a feat such as this is an extraordinary story in itself and one which should interest the reader.

In the fleshy tissue of all coral polyps, sea anemones, jellyfishes and hydrozoans, lie innumerable numbers of capsules which are known to scientists as nematocysts. They are extremely small and can be seen only by means of a microscope. In some of the stony coral polyps, they may only measure 1/50 mm. in length and invariably occur in great numbers throughout the tentacles. There are various types of capsules and each performs a certain job. The stinging or penetrant nematocyst is enveloped by a cell known as a cnidoblast. Simply, the nematocyst can be likened to a coiled spring enclosed in a small inflated rubber bulb. If the rubber were punctured the spring would most certainly shoot out. The same thing occurs with the nematocyst, which is enclosed inside the cnidocil. When an unwary animal brushes against the tentacles of a coral polyp, thousands of microscopic threads are immediately ejected and through these a very potent venom is injected into the prey, which is quickly killed or paralysed. This rather deadly type is not the only kind which occurs in the tissue – others are used for anchorage and some are used for defence. The discharge mechanism of the capsules cannot yet be fully explained but the toxin is believed to be a protein.

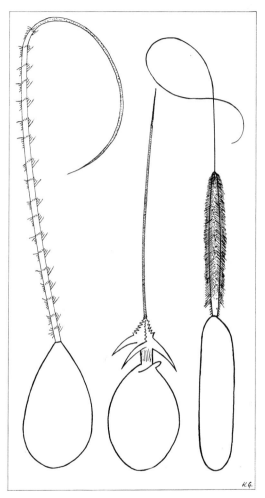

Three types of barbed, penetrant "stinging" capsules (nematocysts). Drawn from photomicrographs.

"Stinging" Coral, *Millepora platyphylla.*

Hydroid, *Aglaophenia cupressina.*

Now that we know how corals sting and capture their prey, we should add a few words about some very closely related types which can cause discomfort to human beings. One known "stinger" is *Millepora platyphylla*, easily recognised by its minute pores and bright yellow and brown colouring. Actually, it is not a true coral and is known to zoologists as a hydrozoan, although it does secrete a calcareous skeleton and contributes to a degree in reef construction. It is quite common on the Reef and if it happens to come in contact with a sensitive part of the body, a tingling or prickling sensation will most certainly be felt. As a point of interest natives at Cocos-Keeling name such hydrozoans *karang gatal* or "itchy corals".

The hydrozoan or hydroid, *Aglaophenia cupressina* (fernlike in appearance and brownish-green in colour), exists in deep pools on the exposed reef flats. It is sometimes called "stinging seaweed" and can cause a little discomfort if accidentally handled. Strangely enough, one clump may cause a burning sensation to the skin, yet another growth a few yards away will give no reaction if touched. The reason is unexplained.

Another hydroid which occurs always in depths of more than 2 fathoms is *Lytocarpus philippinus*. It should never be handled in any circumstances for the pain inflicted by this hydrozoan is severe and, in some cases, an allergic reaction can result from its sting. It is usually found growing beneath coral ledges at about 5 fathoms but has been seen at depths of up to 20 fathoms in Great Barrier Reef waters.

A hydroid which is restricted to moderately deep Reef waters is *Lytocarpus phoeniceus*. This hydrozoan is fernlike in appearance and can inflict a painful sting.

"Stinging" Hydroid, *Lytocarpus philippinus*, Depth 10 fathoms, *Photo—W. Deas.*

SEA ANEMONES
(Actiniaria)

SEA ANEMONES are basically another form of polyp, with a body constructed on the same general plan as that of the corals. Like their close relation, they employ the same simple and intriguing method of capturing prey; they either kill or paralyse by using stinging capsules embedded in their tissue. In addition, the anemones possess a special type of nematocyst (spirocyst) which discharges a holding thread with an adhesive secretion. It is interesting to note that this occurs only in the Actiniaria.

Anemones are found in every ocean, almost from pole to pole, and occur from the very edge of the tideline down to great depths, where they are quite capable of withstanding great pressures and water temperature variations. Their normal method of locomotion is by gliding along on their bases like a worm, or looping over and over like a grub. Some are even capable of swimming by vigorous lashing movements of the tentacles. In all, there is a complete absence of any respiratory or circulatory systems.

Sea anemones do not lack enemies and some animals, such as the naked-gilled sea-slugs (nudibranchs) and flatworms, relish their nematocyst-laden tissue. Remarkable as it may seem, these animals do not suffer any ill-effects from the stinging capsules, and what is even more intriguing is that they are able to transfer them through their own digestive tracts and then out into their tissues without discharging the capsules. The animals then knowingly use them for their own defence.

It is only in the tropical waters of the Barrier Reef region that giant sea anemones are to be found.

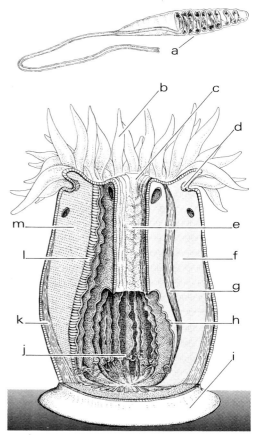

Nematocyst and anatomy of sea anemone. (a) Spirocyst partially discharged. (b) Tentacles. (c) Mouth. (d) Circular muscle and acrorhagi. (e) Gullet. (f) Primary mesentery. (g) Longitudinal muscle of mesentery. (h) Mesenterial filament. (i) Basal disc. (j) Gastro-vascular cavity. (k) Parietal muscle. (l) Gonad. (m) Secondary mesentery.

Giant Barrier Reef Anemone, *Stoichactis haddoni* (nat. size).

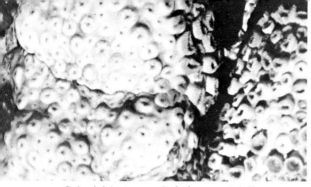

Colonial Anemone, *Palythoa caesia* (x2).

The largest is *Stoichactis kenti*, a veritable giant of its kind, and on the coral banks of the Capricorn Group a single specimen may measure as much as 3 ft. across. Its long slender tentacles (sometimes tipped with red) seem to possess an iridescent greenish or dark bluish hue when exposed to daylight. One is apt to come across groups of individuals living in complete harmony with each other and preferring indentations or crevices of coral boulders. Upon being touched, these anemones swiftly contract and withdraw from sight.

Another large and very closely related Reef anemone is *Stoichactis haddoni*, which reaches a maximum width of about 2 ft. Beadlike tentacles clothe its expanded top (disc) in patches of grey, white, lilac and emerald-green. In this case the individual anemones are widely scattered, living in complete isolation one from another and preferring the outer edge of coral banks. Again, it is an inhabitant of shallow water with its base firmly and deeply anchored in the sand.

By far the most common anemone along the Reef is *Physobrachia ramsayi*, with its long elongated tentacles carrying lobes at their tips. It is normally brownish-red in colour with the tentacles a greyish-white shade towards their tips. Almost invariably it lodges itself deep within the branches of coral growths, where the main body (column) is almost hidden from view. It does not occur in groups and is a little smaller than the two types already mentioned. All can be handled in complete safety and will not sting, their venom not being as irritant as that released by other members of the Actiniaria.

A marine gem, by any standard, is the little Waratah Anemone, *Actinia tenebrosa*, which occurs not only in the Reef region, but is also found along the entire Australian coastline. Being normally a shoreline dweller, a receding tide will leave it exposed in great numbers. It is then that its tentacles are completely withdrawn and a cluster of individuals presents the appearance of brownish-red pebbles. Upon being submerged a radical change takes place; a crowded array of lighter-coloured tentacles emerge from the top of the body, presenting to the eye a creature of exquisite grace and beauty. When closely examined, there is usually found an evenly spaced row of blue, tear-shaped dots around the inside rim of the disc. These are known as acrorhagi and consist of a concentration of spirocysts. Among all its related kind, the waratah anemone is unique in its possession of these little blue areas on its disc, which emit a glow in daylight. The latter have been found not to respond to long-or short-wave ultra-violet light and at present no reason can be given for their association with this particular anemone.

While some examples of strange relationships will be mentioned in another section, the following account has been reserved for comment here. It concerns the three very large Reef anemones already described. Associated with them in a partnership remarkable in Nature is a number of

Anemone, *Physobrachia* and commensal fish, *Amphiprion melanopus* (x2).

strikingly coloured fish. Altogether there are seven different kinds and they belong to three genera (Actinicola, Amphiprion, and Premnas). Sometimes referred to as Clown Fish, they live amongst the stinging tentacles of the anemones and are not affected in any way by the venom released by the nematocysts. Here is a strange and intriguing relationship and one that has puzzled scientists for many years. In fact they seem to derive some benefit from their host and "cuddle" in to the anemone if disturbed in any way. One theory for their presence is that the fish lures unwary prey to the anemone, where it is quickly stung and devoured. In repayment for this, these ornate little fish are left a few tasty morsels. It is very doubtful whether this is the answer to such a strange partnership – the fish seem to derive some nutritional benefit from the tentacles of the anemone. And to confuse matters even more, different clown fish occupy as tenants various kinds of large anemones. Experiments have shown that when a clown fish of another kind is placed in a tank with an anemone and its rightful tenant, the invader is attacked and prevented from approaching the anemone. If the intruder continues to approach the anemone, and tries to take possession of it, a battle to the death occurs, the victor then taking over the tenancy of the anemone. All anemone fish keep extremely well in aquaria.

Until now we have mentioned only those anemones which are true Reef inhabitants and can be touched or handled with impunity. There is one, however, which is purely a sand- or mud-dweller and is common on the fringing reefs and coastline of Queensland. This species, *Actinodendron plumosum* has a sinister reputation and prefers deeper water, its stem or column being normally rooted beneath the sand or mud to a depth of about 12 ins. The top (disc) is densely clothed with short branched tentacles, and is characteristically produced into permanent arm-like lobes. The colour may be in varying shades of light brown and dingy white, but is mostly a stone-grey hue matching the surroundings of its usual habitat. It should not be handled in any circumstances for its venom is very potent and this animal must be regarded as a dangerous "stinger". Fortunately, in the Capricorn Group, it is not a force to be reckoned with but quite a few fishermen along the Queensland coast will have cause to remember *Actinodendron*, and will not forget the painful and burning weal it causes when handled.

A final mention may now be made of quite a strange and unsuspected reaction from a sea anemone source. In this case the culprit, *Rhodactis howesi*, is quite a small variety, measuring only 35 mm. across. It occurs fairly commonly on the northern part of the Reef, but only one small group has so far been found by the writer – on Heron Island coral bank in the Capricorn Group. The body has a rather flattened appearance and is topped with attractive short, lilac-tipped tentacles. In wider parts of the Pacific, where natives draw on much of the marine fauna as a source of food, this little anemone has earned a bad reputation; in American Samoa, for instance, its indiscreet consumption has caused a number of fatalities. Death occurred within 48 hours and appears to have been caused by respiratory failure. Recent research (1960) indicates that the toxic principle in *Rhodactis howesi* is a protein. Luckily for white Australians, who have no similar appetite for such exotic marine foods, the risk of so dire a result is very remote.

The rare and Poisonous Anemone, *Rhodactis howesi* (x6).

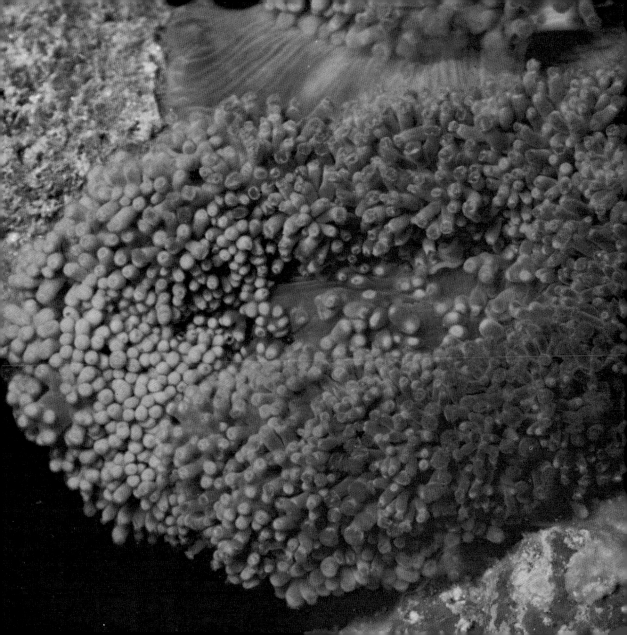

WORMS
(Vermes)

ONE MIGHT NATURALLY ASSUME that for beauty, patterning, and intricate detail, the marine worms could not compete in any way with other Great Barrier Reef inhabitants. Once the word "worm" is mentioned, one visualises long, thin, writhing organisms, better left unmolested in the dark recesses of their retreats. This is an erroneous reaction, for although a few types do resemble terrestrial forms in many ways, there are some strikingly beautiful worms that are the very antithesis of what one expects of such creatures. This is particularly so among those inhabiting tropical seas, and a number forming part of the Reef fauna is no exception.

However, first a little about the worms which are to be found on exposed reef flats. At low tide, the turning over of a coral boulder can reveal one or more of the paper-thin, oval-shaped flatworms (Polycladida). Related to the liver fluke (well known as a parasite of sheep), they range in size from quite small dimensions to veritable giants (up to 75 mm. long). Many are beautifully coloured, and to see a large polyclad swimming freely with sinuous, undulating movements is truly a remarkable sight and is certainly one to remember. No wonder that such displays of action and colour have inspired the popular name of "magic carpet worm".

The flatworms are the most primitive of the group, and the two sexes are combined in single individuals (hermaphroditism). By habit they are carnivorous, feeding upon the living or dead flesh of other marine creatures. They envelop their prey by wrapping themselves around it and then excrete a slime or mucus over the unlucky victim. A funnel-like pharynx can be extruded through the mouth on the underside of the body and the food is digested before it is swallowed. A common Reef species is *Pseudoceros corallophilus*, its cream body bordered with orange and black. It is very delicate and may grow to approximately 37 mm. long.

Perhaps the most striking worm of all along the Reef is the so-called Ribbon Worm, *Baseodiscus quinquelineatus*. Again a frequenter of the exposed coral reefs, it grows to the great length of 10 ft. and has amazing powers of expansion and contraction. When handled, its elongated body immediately starts to contract and thicken. The final state is a loosely tangled and twisted bunch of body loops in which head and tail are indistinguishable. The thin, narrow unsegmented body is whitish, and running along the whole of the back are a number of jet-black, closely set hair lines. It normally lives beneath coral boulders and is very seldom seen in the open. *Baseodiscus* is rarely seen on the southern part of the Reef but is quite common in far northern waters.

Worms of this kind are called nemerteans and a special feature of their anatomy is that they possess a very long proboscis which can be shot out from a sheath near the anterior end of the body with remarkable speed and unerring aim. All are carnivorous and make use of this proboscis in catching their prey.

Also to be found at low tide on the undersides of dead coral slabs and boulders is a bristle-footed worm, *Eurythoe complanata*, which grows to about 5 ins. in length. As with many others of its kind, the creamish body is typically segmented and has an external ringed appearance. A liberal adornment of quite long, needle-sharp, white bristles is concentrated in paired bunches along

Flatworm, *Pseudoceros bedfordi* (x5).

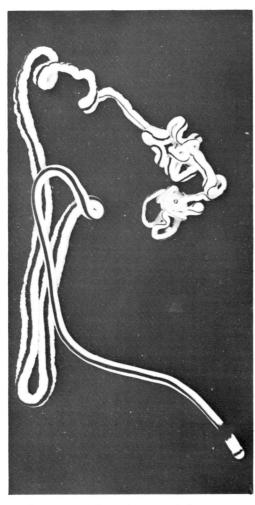

Reef nemertean, *Baseodiscus* sp. (x4).

the sides, giving the worm a most attractive appearance. The same species occurs profusely in southern waters of Australia, but is generally much smaller and salmon-pink in colour. This particular worm is one to be treated with caution: any careless handling causes the bristles to penetrate and break off in the skin, where they may cause severe irritation. Recently, the writer was badly stung between the fingers of his left hand and found it impossible to remove all the embedded portions of the bristles. Almost immediately, there was a marked swelling of the affected parts and the accompanying pain persisted in diminishing degree for about a week after the incident. Possibly the bristles themselves are enough to cause this condition. Whether venom is associated with them remains to be proved, for the reaction is quick and very painful. The possibility of allergy is another factor to be considered when dealing with injuries inflicted by this particular worm.

Among marine worms, those known as sabellids are the most beautiful and showy. Several kinds inhabit Reef waters and are easily recognised by their delicate, flowerlike heads and the soft-walled tubes in which they live. They prefer a location constantly submerged below ledges or in coral caves beyond the edge of the reef. It is here in a greenish-blue domain, 4 to 5 fathoms deep, that the skindiver will frequently discover examples of a form named *Sabellastarte*, attached erect in the silt-covered tubes they fashion as homes. Their beautiful feathery heads extract oxygen from the water and function as well for the netting of minute passing prey. At the slightest stimulation (a touch, a water movement, or even a passing shadow) the worm will retract its long gill-plumes into its tubular home in an instant. In

Head of Feather-duster Worm, *Sabellastarte indica* (x3).

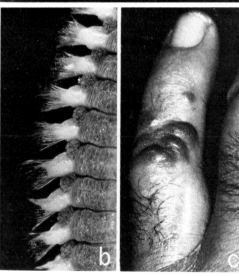

(a) Bristle Worm, *Eurythoe complanata*.
(b) Bundles of setae from *Eurythoe* (x6)
(c) Swelling and blistering after 24 hrs. with a self-inflicted sting from this worm.

this particular group there is no operculum (lid) to close the openings of the tubes when the feathery heads are withdrawn. In temperate waters the same kinds of worms may adopt the gregarious habit of living in groups of five or six, but the tropical forms appear to prefer a solitary existence.

A great Barrier Reef representative of a group known as terebellid worms is technically named *Reteterebella*. Although it was not recognised and described in scientific literature until a few years ago, it was already known as the most conspicuously abundant worm inhabiting the coral reef flats. Thin white or creamish threads (the tentacles) are a common sight protruding from underneath coral boulders and writhing about in search of food particles. This method of questing for food is not so common among marine worms, but it is very effective in obtaining sustenance for the well-nourished body so comfortably housed in its hidden retreat. The turning over of the worm's often bulky shelter discloses to view a rather flabby, swollen creature some 50 to 75 mm. long, with its body composed of a series of closely-set rings. Springing from its head is an incredible tangle of numerous tentacles. A protective casing (hardly a tube) encompasses the main body – an easily-fractured covering constructed of mucus, silt and sand grains. The body colour of the worm can vary from a creamish shade to a bright purplish-blue colour. When fully extended, a set of tufty, orange-red gills are to be seen and these are its most striking feature.

Sometimes seen associated with *Reteterebella queenslandia* is a smaller worm which also makes its home in the sandy casing. Measuring about 15 mm. in length it could be classified as a commensal sharing the food of its host.

Body and tentacles of *Reteterebella queenslandia* (nat. size).

GREAT BARRIER REEF SHELLS
(Mollusca)

SEA-SHELLS have a natural attraction for most people because of their beauty, patterning and delicate shape. All are classified in a group called the Mollusca, which includes a tremendous variation of terrestrial, freshwater, and marine invertebrates. Some of these animals possess shells, some do not, and it is well beyond the scope of this book to do justice to such a fascinating assortment of creatures. The Reef has probably a greater concentration of molluscan life than any other area in the world, for the subtropical and tropical climate of the region offers ideal conditions for the growth and multiplication of these marine animals. It is virtually impossible when exploring a coral bank not to see some of the better known members of this massive group crawling among the coral growths.

The Mollusca can be divided into five classes or sections. The first includes the Chitons or coat-of-mail shells, which occur on the sides of "niggerheads" on the outer edge of reef flats or along the shoreline attached to beach rock, which is usually associated with coral cays. They prefer shallow water and become more active at night. Many are seaweed eaters (herbivores) and are easily identified by their outer shell, which consists of eight plates resembling the steel plates of a suit of armour. A large chiton, *Acanthozostera gemmata*, exists on the Reef and is very abundant in the Capricorn-Bunker area.

The second group is known as the Gastropoda and consists of the univalves: Cowries, Cones, Volutes, Strombs, Sea-slugs, etc. This massive assortment is well represented on the Reef and it is in this section that the most ornate members are found. Shells with exquisite texture, brilliance of colour, and even some with a sinister reputation, are all to be found in this particular group of molluscs.

The bivalves constitute the third group and are represented by oysters, pipis, scallops, etc. This group is referred to as the Pelecypoda and includes the largest bivalve in the world, the giant clam to which many a diver's death has rather rashly been attributed. The sought-after and coveted Gold-lip Pearl Oyster exists only at the northern tip of the Reef and is an outstanding member of this particular group.

Elephant-tusk shells do not seem to be a very interesting mollusc but they make up the fourth and smallest section of the Mollusca. Essentially bottom-dwellers, they prefer to burrow into the sand. This group is known as the Scaphopoda.

The last section consists of the octopus, squid, cuttlefish, and pearly nautilus, a partnership known as the Cephalopoda. The first three occur in quite large numbers on the Reef and, although unfortunately at the present time very little is known about the Reef octopus, it is a spectacular mollusc and will be dealt with a little later in this book. Many fishermen have cause to remember the cuttlefish, which grows to a considerable size. In these waters it takes a fiendish delight in stealing fish from them, usually at a frustrating moment – just when the fish is about to be pulled into the boat. With lightning speed it will appear from out of the depths and remove the fish in an instant. The shoreline of all coral cays is strewn with their cuttle-bones. The writer has never seen a living nautilus in Reef waters, although shells without the animals are very common and are washed up on the beaches after heavy south-east weather.

"Nivigena melwardi", the albino form of *Cypraea cribraria* (x7).

COWRIES
(Cypraeadae)

COWRY SHELLS are renowned for their beauty, unsurpassable polish, and attractive shape. Possibly the best known of all molluscs these outstanding shells are cherished by amateur shell collectors the world over. Slow moving and extremely shy, these molluscs feed on small crustaceans and a great variety of rather small marine organisms. Their eggs are laid in a single mass (from about 100 to more than 1,500), each capsule measuring approximately 2 to 4 mm. in length. As a general rule they hatch in one or two weeks and the larvae are dispersed into the surrounding waters where they go through a free-swimming larval stage. At its conclusion, the juveniles then settle in a suitable area and wander very little from this spot, living amongst seaweed, coral, and sand.

At low water, cowries usually retreat beneath coral ledges or seek shelter in crevices and indentations of coral boulders. It is during the night that they are to be seen in great numbers crawling over the exposed coral in search of food.

Key to Cowries (opposite page).

(a) *Cypraea argus*	(b) *Ovula ovum*
(c) *Volva volva*	(d) *Cypraea tigris*
(e) *Cypraea vitellus*	(f) *Cypraea eburnea*
(g) *Cypraea erosa*	(h) *Cypraea carneola*
(i) *Cypraea isabella*	(j) *Cypraea facifer*
(k) *Cypraea moneta*	(l) *Cypraea annulus*
(m) *Calpurnus verrucosus*	(n) *Cypraea cribraria*
(o) *Cypraea staphylaea*	(p) *Cypraea helvolva*
(q) *Cypraea asellus*	

Underside of Tiger Cowry, *C. tigris*.

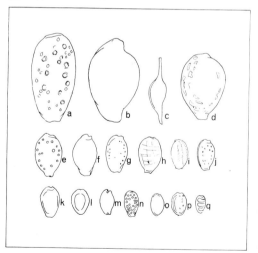

Cowry shells (slightly less than nat. size).

VOLUTES
(Volutidae)

RENOWNED for their tremendous variation in size, colour, and patterning, the volutes are common inhabitants of Reef waters. These beautiful creatures spend most of their time buried under the sand in coral lagoons and in deeper water off the edge of coral reefs. They usually emerge at night to forage for food, which consists of bivalves and other molluscs.

The largest Reef species is the melon or baler shell, *Melo*, which may grow to about 15 ins. in length and weigh up to 4 or 5 lb. They are rarely seen during daylight for the melon shell buries itself in the sand and only a fraction of the shell may be seen. During dull weather it is sometimes seen crawling over the sand using its muscular foot as a means of locomotion.

One beautiful little volute (maximum size about 75 mm.) is *Cymbiolacca pulchra*. Commonly known as the Heron Island Volute, it occurs only in the Capricorn region. Many other larger volutes are brought up from deep water by trawl nets used by fishermen. These rarer types are nearly all brightly coloured.

Key to Volutes (opposite page).
(a) *Volutoconus grossi*
(b) *Cymbiolacca complexa*
(c) *Cymbiolacca wisemani*
(d) *Cymbiolacca cracenta*
(e) *Amoria maculata*
(f) *Aulicina sophiae*
(g) *Cymbiolacca pulchra*
(h) *Cymbiolacca wisemani* (*randalli* form).

Carol's Volute, *Amoria maculata*, alive.

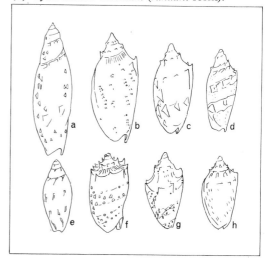

Volute shells (nat. size).

CONE SHELLS
(Conidae)

CONE SHELLS are a highly specialised type of gastropod and belong to a group known as Toxoglossa or "arrow-tongues". All are carnivorous and employ a most unusual method of catching their prey – in fact it is unique among all molluscs and has intrigued scientists for many years. They are also the only gastropods in the world capable of directly causing death to human beings.

But first a little about the anatomy of the animal which is housed inside the shell. When the mollusc is viewed alive, it may extend quite a length out of the shell. The siphon, sometimes ringed with orange (as in the case of *Conus textile*), is used as a sensory organ and actually picks up the scent of the victim. In many cases the cone buries itself and only the tip of the siphon is seen protruding a few millimetres out of the sand. A tubular and mobile organ called the proboscis is extended and used to deliver the coup-de-grâce and must actually touch the victim. Through this fleshy part of the animal, minute darts called radular teeth are projected and these can be likened to a hypodermic needle, for venom is forced through the hollow, needle-sharp teeth. The darts are barbed at the top and resemble an arrow tip. The cone may use only one, but if this fails to stupefy the victim, others are held in reserve in a part of the animal known as the radular sac. The writer, in dissecting the animals of various species of these gastropods, has found more than 20 radular teeth in cones such as *Conus striatus* and *Conus textile*.

Some are particularly dangerous – a few with a bad reputation are the fish-eating types, *Conus geographus*, *Conus tulipa*, *Conus striatus*, *Conus*

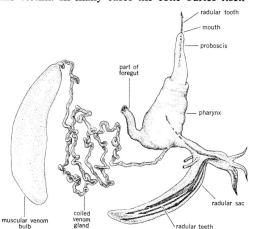 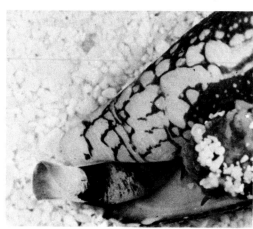

(Left) Venom apparatus of a typical cone. (Right) Close-up of *Conus omaria*.

Textile Cone, *Conus textile*, with siphon fully extended (x4).

magus and *Conus catus*. It is believed that these fish-eating species are the most deadly to humans and the potency of their venom is far greater than that of other members of the group.

The venom released by some of the cones is very toxic indeed. Fatalities have resulted from stings by *Conus geographus*, and medical reports at Western Samoa and New Caledonia indicate that severe stingings from this particular species have occurred in these areas. When a victim is stung, a sharp pain is felt where the radular tooth enters the flesh. The area then becomes numb and discoloured. Severe pain may then result and then vision, hearing, and speech are usually affected. In severe cases, complete paralysis of the voluntary muscles ensues. Death is caused mainly by respiratory failure.

Egg mass of *Conus striatus* (x2).

Rather conflicting reports have been given about the Textile Cone, *Conus textile*, but it has usually been regarded as a harmless member of the group. Recent experiments with this species have shown it to be dangerous and should be handled with extreme care.

Key to Cones (opposite page).
(a) *Conus (Cylinder) textile*
(b) *Conus (Gastridium) geographus*
(c) *Conus (Rhombus) imperialis*
(d) *Conus (Strioconus) striatus*
(e) *Conus (Rhizoconus) vexillum*
(f) *Conus (Regiconus) aulicus*
(g) *Conus (Cleobula) figulina*
(h) *Conus (Rhizoconus) miles*
(i) *Conus (Tuliparia) tulipa*
(j) *Conus (Chelyconus) catus*
(k) *Conus (Pionoconus) suturatus*
(l) *Conus (Virroconus) imperator*

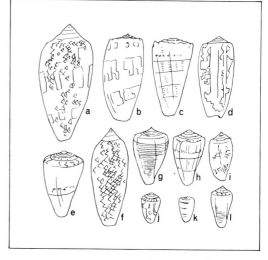

Cone shells (nat. size).

STROMBS
(Strombidae)

STROMBS are characterised by a strong muscular foot armed with a spur-like operculum which is used to close the opening of the shell when the animal withdraws inside.

The Spider Shell, *Lambis lambis*, is a particularly common species and is found along the entire length of the Reef system. When placed on its back it will quickly extend its long and powerful foot and place it under the shell, then, with a jerky movement, it will force itself over. The strombs are truly the acrobats of the molluscan world. With this particular shell, the underside and interior are of a beautiful orange-red colour and this species is prized by shell collectors. The

Strombus gibberulus, alive.

outside is covered with a layer of growth (periostracum) which acts as a form of camouflage.

Another stromb which occurs in great numbers on all exposed coral reefs is the Luhu or Redmouthed Stromb, *Strombus luhuanus*. The distinct notch in the outside lip of the shell indicates its close relationship with other strombs. Although it is a rather formidable-looking animal when viewed with its foot fully extended, it is quite harmless and can be handled in complete safety.

Key to Strombs (opposite page).
(a) *Strombus (Lentigo) lentiginosus*
(b) *Strombus (Euprotomus) aratrum*
(c) *Strombus (Conomurex) luhuanus*
(d) *Strombus (Dolomena) variabilis*
(e) *Strombus (Gibberulus) gibberulus*
(f) *Strombus (Doxander) vittatus*
(g) *Strombus (Laevistrombus) canarium*

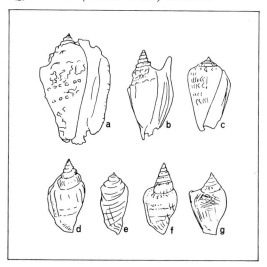

Stromb shells (nat. size).

BIVALVES
(Pelecypoda)

GREAT BARRIER REEF bivalves constitute a major section of molluscan life to be found in the region. Shells from colder waters are generally unattractive and cannot compare with these tropical and sub-tropical species for beauty of form and colour.

The two valves are joined together by a hinge, and one or two powerful muscles hold the shells in place. They are a very diverse group; some can swim and others can bore into rock, but nearly all live in mud or sand and move by means of a muscular foot.

The Swimming File-Shell, *Promantellum parafragile*, or, as it is known in the Reef area, the

Lima, *Promantellum parafragile,* alive.

Lima, propels itself through the water with a jerky movement. It possesses a set of scarlet tentacles which can never be completely withdrawn inside the shell. Its locomotion is accomplished by the sudden snapping together of the two valves of the shell.

Key to Shells (opposite page).
(a) *Amusium balloti*
(b) *Laciolina quoyi*
(c) *Solen aureomaculatus*
(d) *Trisidos yongei*
(e) *Gloripallium pallium*
(f) *Fragum unedo*
(g) *Lioconcha castrensis*
(h) *Lentillaria paytenorum*
(i) *Regozara flava*
(j) *Tapes literata*
(k) *Scutarcopagia linguafelis*

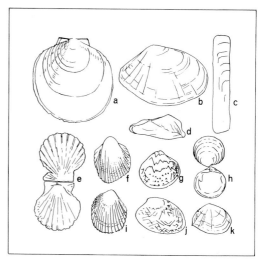

Bivalve shells (slightly less than nat. size).

REEF CLAMS
(Tridacnidae)

IN QUITE A FEW CASES with bivalve molluscs, the animal which inhabits the shell is more spectacular and colourful than the shell itself. Although many of these bivalves adorn the desks and mantelpieces of amateur conchologists, to see them in their natural habitat and in their living state with the animal fully expanded is an unforgettable experience.

Horse-hoof Clam, *Hippopus hippopus*.

The largest bivalve in the world is the giant clam, *Tridacna gigas*. It is to be found towards the northern end of the Reef, where it grows to more than 4 ft. in length, and its weight may exceed 500 lb. It is usually found in relatively deep water, about 4 fathoms and over, and its fleshy mantle (an olive-green in colour) is not quite as spectacular as that of other members of the Tridacnidae.

A much smaller clam, *Tridacna maxima*, is literally strewn all over a reef flat. It occurs in great numbers in the Capricorn-Bunker Groups and is found from East Africa to eastern Polynesia, except Hawaii. Often seen in groups, individual specimens measure about 13 in. in length. Owing to the tremendous variations of colour with this particular species, it is the most conspicuous member of the group.

The Burrowing Clam, *Tridacna crocea*, is a small species and occupies coral boulders. In some cases it occurs in groups of about five or six. It attains a length of approximately 4 in. and is not as colourful as its close relation, *Tridacna maxima*. By a sort of grinding process it becomes embedded in coral boulders and in many cases the open margin of the shell valves lies flush with the surface.

On fringing reefs is to be found yet another type of clam. The Horse-hoof Clam, *Hippopus hippopus*, grows to about 12 in. in length and usually possesses an olive-green mantle. It is a particularly robust species and occurs in great numbers on these exposed reef flats. It is also to to be found on the northern section of the Reef and is quite common on Green Island but is not known to exist in the Capricorn-Bunker Groups or further south.

Reef Clam, *Tridacna maxima*.

NAKED-GILLED SEA-SLUGS
(Nudibranchia)

NAKED-GILLED SEA-SLUGS or nudibranchs are just another marine assemblage which helps to make up the massive phylum, Mollusca. They are "shellfish without shells", a strange statement to make and one which may confuse the reader. To clarify matters, these ornate little creatures do not possess an outer shell as others do, and at first sight one tends to disbelieve that they are true molluscs. They appear to be completely divorced from any other known group of marine life.

A striking feature with nudibranchs is the cluster of branched gill-plumes which occur on the back towards the posterior end of the animal. It is quite apparent that their name "naked-gill" originates from this feature. If touched, these gills can be withdrawn with considerable speed into a cavity.

Many nudibranchs are carnivorous. Some feed on coelenterates, which they appear to relish and, as stated earlier, they are not affected by the nematocysts present in the tissue which they devour. They are mainly shallow-water dwellers but one particular species is oceanic and floats on the surface of the water.

A great number of these shell-less forms of marine life is to be found on the Reef. As with much of the marine fauna which exists in these tropical waters, they occur in a varied assortment of colours and patterns and seem to overshadow creatures which are located in southern waters. The photographer finds it hard to do justice to this particular group for they are so splendrous and bizarre. Even with the latest photographic techniques, the finished colour transparency will sometimes be found disappointing compared with the impression the animal creates when alive.

A very spectacular northern species is the "Dancing Lady" or "Spanish Dancer", *Hexabranchus imperialis*. Its glorious, deep orange-red body, ringed with white, with bright yellow markings down the middle of its top surface, make it probably one of the most beautiful nudibranchs to be seen on a coral reef. It can grow to a length of about 12 in. and is the Reef's largest nudibranch. To view this unusual animal in an aquarium, and watch its undulating movements when swimming, is a fascinating experience. It has a wide distribution in tropical seas and is also found in northern New South Wales waters.

Chromodoris quadricolor is a relatively small nudibranch, about 70 mm. in length and is easily recognised by its blackish and vivid blue-striped body, ringed with bright orange. It is a common inhabitant of exposed coral banks.

Glaucus is an animal not associated with the shore. It occurs in tropical and sub-tropical waters and during the summer months is occasionally washed up on New South Wales beaches. This nudibranch actually floats on the surface of the water and although this may seem unusual, its underside is towards the sky. In other words it is upside down, crawling on the undersurface of the water film. The dorsal surface is of a silvery iridescent colour and its belly surface is an intense blue. It is a most unusual and beautiful little nudibranch.

The group is unique, and it is impossible to give descriptions of even a small percentage of the animals involved. The abovementioned nudibranchs are fairly common on the Reef but many others are still unknown as yet to marine zoologists.

Nudibranch, *Gymnodoris ceylonica* (x4).

THE OCTOPUS
(Cephalopoda)

THIS QUAINT MEMBER of the molluscan group is far removed in form from its better-known relatives. Over eons, its unusual body has been evolved until there is a complicated union of head and foot, as its Greek group name implies. There are many kinds of octopuses in the shallower waters of all seas, but none is as large as popular legend would have us believe. Strange as it may seem, off the Australian coastline there are only two species which are known to have caused deaths, and the animals are very small and do not look fearsome in any way. In fact, both are striking in appearance. One is the southern species, *Hapalochlaena maculosa* (sometimes called the ringed octopus), and the other is a closely related northern type, *Hapalochlaena lunulatus*. With the tentacles fully extended, both measure no more than about 5 in. across. At present, there is no known species on the Great Barrier Reef which can be considered dangerous to human beings.

The most frequently encountered octopus on the coral banks along the Reef has slender, tapering tentacles which have a span of 2 ft. or more. It is normally coloured an orange-red blotched with whitish areas. Although not so far positively identified by marine zoologists, this particular octopus is suspected to be closely related to a well known one from Hawaiian waters. The Reef form, like many of its kind in other parts, occupies a so-called nest in some convenient cavity it clears for itself in the surface of a coral bank. Such sites may have a low craterlike mouth, with the margins comprised of small débris which often includes empty bivalve shells. Foraging over a coral bank exposed at night by tidal waters appears to be a regular practice, and the octopus usually prefers the outer edge of a reef in its search for food. If disturbed in any way, a quick change of body colour is not beyond the cephalopod's powers.

The colour-change mechanism is present in its close relative, the cuttlefish, and the agents responsible for these changes are numerous cells lodged in the outer layers of the skin, known as chromatophores. They vary in diameter from a fraction of a millimetre to at least 5 mm. in diameter in the case of some members of the group. Their expansion and contraction result from the action of minute muscles that are attached to the outer perimeter of the cell. When the muscles are contracted, the chromatophore appears as a large flat plate. When the muscles relax, the pigment is concentrated. Even after death, the chromatophores of some cephalopods can function actively for as long as 30 minutes. The cuttlefish may be observed bringing about changes in colouring to match the objects over which it swims. With the octopus, the colour changes seem to flow over the body, and have to be seen to be believed.

All octopuses are carnivorous and possess a pair of beaklike jaws, powerful enough to tear prey to pieces. A paralysing toxin injected from special glands also assist the attacker when dealing with its captives. Its usual diet is fish and crustaceans, but octopuses are not averse to feeding on the flesh of molluscs.

There have been highly coloured but quite untrue accounts of large octopuses and sea-snakes attacking divers in tropical northern Australian waters. Both are, however, not aggressive to humans.

Barrier Reef Octopus, Heron Island.

CRABS AND RELATIONS
(Crustacea)

IN PARTS OF the Great Barrier Reef there is a seemingly endless variety of crustaceans. There is no area from the actual shoreline to the outer limits of a coral reef where crabs and their relations do not occur. Many, of course, are cryptic forms that retreat into the sandy or silted surface – others shelter from the scorching sun beneath coral boulders, while still others seek recesses deep in coral growths. It would take volumes to give an outline of all crustaceans which are found in the region, and only a few of the more easily recognised types will be dealt with in this present account.

In the first shallow pool on any coral reef the erratic movements of small shells will attract attention. A close examination shows that these are tenanted by tiny Hermit Crabs, usually the common species, *Clibanarius virescens*. These agile little crustaceans might be described as the comics of their domain. Hermit crabs, as with all others of their kind, have a soft body (abdomen) lacking the tough shelly covering which protects their head portion and front limbs. They live continually in their abodes and there is never any shortage of accommodation. If a new and larger shell is not readily available for housing their growing bodies, they are not averse to thieving a shelter occupied by a living mollusc, which is attacked and dragged from its legitimate abode.

The hermit crab's changing from one shell to another is an unusual little drama and a short story in itself. One empty shell after another is carefully examined and inspected with the finesse of an expert. When this window-shopping is completed and the crab is quite satisfied that the shell will provide adequate living space, he moves opposite to the opening of his new home. Then with remarkable speed the transfer is accomplished. Caution born of a long evolutionary battle for survival has warned the hermit crab that any delayed movement would leave its vulnerable soft hind body open to attack from predators.

Farther out from the shoreline on any tidal flat of a coral bank are to be found much larger hermit crabs. The largest is a brilliant orange-red and white-spotted kind, *Dardanus megistos*. The insatiable appetite of hermit crabs may be gauged from the writer's experience of this particular species, which on numerous occasions has been observed for long periods in aquaria. Small pieces of fish, prawn, and even small molluscs are soon devoured by this inveterate scavenger.

A strange relationship occurs with the hermit crab, *Dardanus deformis*, which transports the anemone, *Calliactis polypus*, on its shelly abode. This strange kind of partnership is not unique, for in northern waters there is another little-understood case of a hermit crab found associating with a certain kind of sponge growth.

As well as the truly marine kinds of hermit crabs there are other highly specialised ones which have all but deserted the sea. These are the so-called Land Hermits, and while two kinds, *Coenobita perlatus* and *Coenobita rugosa*, inhabit widely separated coral islet cays along the Reef, they are more prolific in the Coral Sea region. The

Key to crabs (opposite page).
Top left—Spanner Crab, *Ranina ranina*
  ($\frac{1}{3}$ nat. size).
Top right—Red-eyed Crab, *Eriphia sebana*
  (nat. size).
Bottom—Ghost Crab, *Ocypode ceratophthalma*
  (x2).

Crabs – three contrasting kinds.

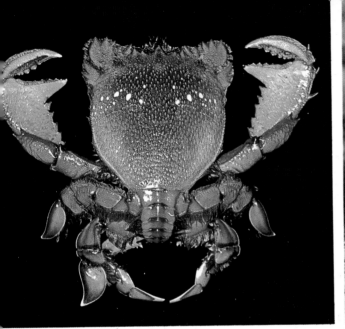

firstnamed is of a bright scarlet colour and the other has a rather creamish body hue with overtones of mauve-to-purple on the limbs and claws (chelae). They are the most hardy and formidable members of the hermit crab group – shoreline scavengers equipped with strong bulbous claws who prefer to hunt for their prey at night. Like their marine cousins they use portable shell abodes, but in this case their housing requirements come from the jetsam of the shoreline. So highly specialised are they that only a minimum of moisture from land sources is required for them to survive, and their gills are so modified that they can actually breathe some air. The one last link with the sea from which they migrated is that the females must enter the water in order to release the larval young from their eggs. Here the development stages are passed through until the time arrives for them to go ashore and lead the normal life of their kind.

Sand-dwellers, the Ghost Crabs, *Ocypode ceratophthalma* and *Ocypode cordimana*, make their homes above high-water mark and burrow about 3 ft. down in the sand. They are night scavengers and are easily identified by their long eyestalks which characterise the group, Ocypodidae. Both species are also found on New South Wales beaches as well as on all the coral cays of the Reef. Telltale, neatly-piled little humps of sand mark the spots on the beach where they have burrowed.

On the coral reefs, well out from the shoreline, is to be found the truly marine domain of the crabs. Here one may take barely a step without observing quite a number of conspicuous kinds. Progress is constantly challenged by the plentiful blue-green Swimming Crab, *Thalamita stimpsoni*, which, if unable to make a swift retreat, will halt with its menacing, sharp-pointed claws upraised. Another challenger barring an intruder's way in like manner is a more thick-bodied crab, *Eriphia sebana*, with bright red eyes and much larger claws.

A truly rare find is an example of the Blood-spotted Crab, *Carpilius maculatus*, with a smooth, rich creamish body which may measure up to 8 in. in width. It has a wide distribution and occurs throughout the tropical Pacific. Because of its striking colouration, it has an attraction for native islanders and in Western Samoa it is a common sight to see the decorative dried shells (carapaces) being sold as souvenirs in the market-places.

While almost constantly present where Reef corals abound, the little Gall Crab, *Hapalocarcinus marsupialis*, evades discovery by all but the initiated. By some extraordinary quirk of Nature the female is destined to spend her adult life imprisoned in a gall-like growth among the branches of certain types of coral. At a very young stage she comes to rest in a selected spot, and in some unexplained manner causes the growing coral to form, around her, two thin calcareous walls. When these finally meet at their extremities they leave only tiny apertures for communication with the outside. Water currents induced by the now imprisoned female convey to her oxygen for breathing as well as the minute forms of marine life on which she feeds. Comparatively minute males, barely 4 mm. in body width, lead a free life outside among the coral branches, and are tiny enough to gain access to their spouses through the small apertures of their prisons.

Possibly, one of the most intriguing of all Barrier Reef crustaceans is the Spanner Crab,

Land Hermit Crab, *Coenobita perlatus* (x2), One Tree Island.

Ranina ranina. It prefers to live and burrow into the soft ocean bottom with its long-peduncled eyes protruding out of the sand. The crabs are often brought up by line fishermen in Reef waters and make excellent eating. The shovel-shaped terminal joints of the legs make this crab the most highly adapted for its mode of life. The limbs are used for burrowing backwards into the sand, where the owner lies in wait for passing prey. The spanner crab is also quite common in New South Wales waters.

Some of the more attractive members of the deeper reef flat pools do not display themselves at low water. They normally retreat into recesses among coral growths, but will on occasions be found by a diligent searcher. One of these is an outstanding kind of shrimp and a very colourful crustacean. The Banded Shrimp, *Stenopus hispidus* has a body about 3 in. long and this, with the limbs, bears a thorn-like covering of short spines. The delicate front limbs bear rather large claws and are quite elongated. These and the many branches of threadlike antennae are kept fully extended while the shrimp is swimming, and produce a most artistic effect. The translucent body is a striking orange-pink with broad red bands, and all the limbs are similarly decorated.

The colourful crayfish of the Reef have received scant mention in any popular book on the region. Some confusion, too, has arisen over the correct vernacular name that should be applied to these large tropical crustaceans. At times the term Spiny Lobster has been used, but preference in the present account is for the name crayfish – the name used by Reef fishermen and all others who have had a close local association with it. These crayfish, as now called, can often be found by

skindivers in fairly shallow water over the margins of coral banks, but may also very occasionally be met with when left by the tide to shelter in some pool on a reef flat. Unlike other better-known marine crayfish, the tropical kinds will not enter traps and can only be speared or captured by hand. For these reasons it is doubtful if they will ever be the basis of a commercial fishery.

The inaccessibility of his quarry poses quite a problem for the skindiver in search of these tropical crayfish. His search is directed to narrow spaces below the overhang of coral platforms or to deep retreats among the growths in coral caves.

Three kinds of crayfish are known to occur in the Reef waters. Perhaps the most spectacular is the Painted Crayfish, *Panulirus versicolor*, which has a wide distribution in the Indo-West-Pacific region. It is easily recognised by its predominantly olive-green body and the decorative colour pattern on the carapace and the hind body (abdomen). Added to this is the black-and-white striping along the limbs, giving to it quite a distinctive appearance. Another, slightly less spectacular species, *Panulirus longipes*, has an overall purplish to brownish coloured body, with the hind part marked with large white spots. The limbs are also streaked or spotted with white. Like the firstnamed this crayfish also has a wide range, being known in the Indo-Pacific from East Africa and eastwards into Polynesia. The third known Reef crayfish, *Panulirus ornatus*, is possibly the easiest to identify. It has a blotchy carapace and limbs with transverse bands of black and yellow. The plates of the hind body are quite smooth and spotted on their sides. It is generally a rarer type than the other Reef crayfish and more likely to be found in northern waters.

The Reef Hermit Crab, *Dardanus megistos* (x2).

ECHINODERMS
(Echinodermata)

THE ECHINODERMATA include starfishes, sea-urchins, feather-stars, brittle-stars and sea-cucumbers or bêche-de-mer. All are exclusively marine and are found generally on the ocean bottom, in all depths from the shallows to the greatest oceanic trenches. More than 5,300 species have already been recognised and named.

STARFISHES
(Asteroidea)

THE CONVENTIONAL five-rayed starfishes are the best known type of echinoderm and many of the interesting features of the group are seen in them. One such feature is the apparent radial arrangement of the body structures. However, there are always one or two structures that do not follow the radial pattern shown by so many of the organs, such as the tube-feet, the reproductive organs, or the skeletal plates, and so on. This tendency to have the body structures disposed like the hub and spokes of a wheel with the "hub" in the central body area and the "spokes" along the starfish's arms, is characteristic. Those remarkable echinoderm structures, the waving tube-feet seen in the grooves on the lower sides of the arms, follow such a radial pattern. It is only when the inner structures of this hydraulically-operated system are looked at and followed along the radial canal in the arm round the intake point at the top of the single stone canal to the asymmetrically-placed madreporitic plate (lying between the arms on the upper surface of the body) that the hidden bilateral symmetry shows itself.

The starfish's method of capturing and devouring prey is very interesting and is featured in most popular accounts so there is no need to describe it here in detail. It is not an uncommon sight on the Reef to see a starfish envelop a bivalve (such as an oyster), force the shell valves apart, and then extrude its stomach into the opening between the gaping valves. The bivalve is probably poisoned and finally digested externally by the starfish and then taken in, in a fluid state. Most asteroids are carnivorous and feed on snails, molluscs, crustaceans, polychaetes, and other echinoderms. In some cases they have been known to devour fish. They are also the ocean's "vacuum-cleaner" and consume dead bodies or the rotting flesh of animals which may litter the ocean bottom.

Asteroids have remarkable powers of regeneration. Parts of the arms can be regenerated and even destroyed parts of the central disc can be replaced. *Linckia* is a classic example of this remarkable process for it is able to cast off its arms close to the base of the disc. Each severed arm is then capable of regenerating a new disc and missing rays. At this stage of growth where the cast off arm is large and the four new arms are just starting to form, it is known as a comet. In certain species the comet will still retain the exact colouring of the adult but in many other reef asteroids regenerating arms assume juvenile colouring while regrowing, and the starfish is difficult to identify. The process of maturing is quite slow, some species take up to 12 months to be fully restored to adult form from this comet stage.

One can easily pick out the vivid blue *Linckia laevigata* on any coral reef. This large starfish (it can grow to about 12 in. across) is fairly common

Nardoa novaecaledoniae, a conspicuous starfish on reef flats (nat. size).

and has a wide distribution throughout the Indo-Pacific. Its close relative, *Linckia guildingii*, is of a drab greyish colour and is also found in protected coral pools or scattered along any coral reef. Its arms are much thinner than those of *Linckia laevigata*. Both these starfishes seem to prefer shallow water and are rarely seen below depths of about four fathoms.

Nardoa novaecaledoniae is possibly the most common starfish to be found on the Reef. It is virtually impossible, when fossicking on a coral reef, to miss seeing this strikingly-marked echinoderm. With tonings of orange on the raised tubicles and browny-green in between, it is often seen curled around coral growths or sheltering on the sandy bottom beside boulders. A closely related species, *Nardoa pauciforis*, grows to a larger size but has essentially the same colouring.

Another remarkable Reef starfish (possibly the most unusual of all in the area) is known as the Crown of Thorns Starfish, *Acanthaster planci*. Many will know its name because of the great deal of publicity it has received in reference to the destruction of coral reefs. Seeming to prefer branched corals, *Acropora*, it envelops the growth and in a short period of time leaves only a bleached calcium carbonate skeleton behind after feeding. *Acanthaster* has a wide distribution in tropical waters and is found along the entire length of the Great Barrier Reef. It also has an evil reputation as a stinger and is regarded as dangerous, the top surface of the body and arms being covered with sharp spines (about 50 mm. in length), which can cause a painful wound if they happen to penetrate the flesh. The sting is very similar to that inflicted by the sea-urchin, *Diadema setosum*. Venom is thought to be associated with the spines of *Acanthaster* but as yet it is not fully understood how it enters the victim. This species prefers warmer water and at the present time is found in plague proportions towards the northern end of the Reef.

Very little is known about *Acanthaster's* early development but it is thought that certain gastropods, such as *Charonia*, feed on the larval stages of the Crown of Thorns. In the northern area the lack of molluscs is quite evident when one examines a coral reef flat at low water. (This is probably due to large numbers being taken off by commercial shell-collectors.) It would seem to indicate that there is a connection between the two and that the natural balance has been upset. It is interesting to note that, on the reefs at Fiji, New Caledonia, and Western Samoa, this starfish is particularly abundant. This is probably caused by the lack of molluscs in these areas, for in many cases the fleshy animals of gastropods are used as food by the natives. In the Capricorn-Bunker Groups, *Acanthaster*, fortunately, is not common, but has been seen at One Tree Island, Broomfield Reef, Fitzroy Reef, and Lady Musgrave Island. In these localities only isolated examples have been observed, at depths of about 2 or 3 fathoms. At the Saumarez Reefs, Kenn Reefs, Cato Island, and Chesterfield Reefs, it is practically non-existent and only isolated examples are to be seen in fairly deep water. Strange as it may seem, when the starfish was viewed in these little-visited localities it did not appear to be feeding on corals, and growths nearby were not eaten in any way. Possibly an abundance of other food which the species may prefer is available and this seems to indicate that a more harmonious balance has been achieved on these virgin reefs. A possible explanation would be that it only attacks corals as a last resort, when other foods are in short supply.

Crown of Thorns Starfish, *Acanthaster planci*, Broomfield Reef.

SEA-URCHINS
(Echinoidea)

THE SEA-URCHIN shows its relationship with starfishes and other echinoderms in the five-rayed pattern of many of its structures, such as the pattern of the pores for its tube-feet. The name Echinoidea is derived from the Greek word, *echinos*, meaning hedgehog, and the urchin's body, covered by a mass of spines, can be likened to this animal in appearance. However, not all sea-urchins have fine short spines like the hedgehog. In some species the spines are long and needle-like, and some urchins even have very thick and blunted ones, as in the species illustrated on the opposite page.

Another distinguishing feature of sea-urchin structure is the fusion of the skeleton plates into a body cover or test. When the urchin dies and the spines fall off, the test remains and these ornamental, circular "sea-eggs", as they are often called, are quite common on the shores of coral cays. The live sea-urchin is able to move its spines, which are mounted on small protuberances on the test to form ball-and-socket joints. Movement of the spines is brought about by the action of rings of muscles around the base of each individual spine. Tube-feet also aid in their locomotion.

With many sea-urchins, the diet consists of seaweed and molluscs, while some deeper-water species are detritus feeders, consuming minute organic particles contained in the bottom ooze. If the animal is broken open a remarkable jaw apparatus called "Aristotle's lantern" is revealed. It projects downwards slightly through the mouth where five teeth can be seen. The "lanterns" structure consists of five calcareous sections called pyramids, and each of these segments is shaped like a barbed arrowhead, with the point projecting towards the mouth.

Many species of urchins are to be found on the Reef, either on exposed coral banks or in moderately deep water. A very common sea-urchin, usually found wedged in indentations of the surface of coral boulders, is *Echinometra mathaei*. Its spines are moderately short and pointed, and several colour variations occur in this species. The spines can vary from a light colour to brown (some may even have dark brownish black spines with light tips). *Echinometra* has a wide distribution in tropical seas and is to be seen along the length of the Reef, West Australia, and northern New South Wales. It is considered to be one of the most common sea-urchins in the world.

Extremely long, tapering needle-sharp spines make *Diadema setosum* the most spectacular sea-urchin on the Reef system. It is not common on the southern section, but is to be found in great numbers in the more tropical northern waters of the region. It is particularly prevalent at Low Isles. Specimens as large as 12 in. across, measured from spine-tip to spine-tip, have been found. Juveniles of this species may have spines with alternating dark and light bands whereas adults show a uniformly violet-black colour.

The needle-spined urchin, *Diadema*, is dangerous and should never be handled. It is almost impossible to pick the animal up without getting a few of the spines embedded in the flesh. If this happens an immediate stinging pain is felt, and the spines are very difficult to remove. It seems likely that venom is associated with the spines, for the writer has had two unpleasant encounters with this echinoderm and on one occasion nearly lost his left hand through infection.

Slate-pencil Urchin, *Heterocentrotus mamillatus* (x2).

FEATHER-STARS
(Crinoidea)

OF ALL ECHINODERMS the crinoids are the most delicate and exquisite, and their lineage goes far back in geological time. A stalked type called the sea lily, prospered during the Paleozoic era. Another type of crinoid, the feather-star, is unstalked, except during the earliest stages of its life history and many local species belong to the Comatulid group. Unfortunately little is known about Barrier Reef feather-stars at present and they are generally considered the most difficult of all Reef animals to photograph. Like their relations, the brittle-stars, they throw off their feathery arms on the slightest provocation. All of them are capable of losing their colour if aggravated, and will foul an aquarium in a short space of time. Sometimes this reaction is instantaneous, and waves of colour pigment will be released by the feather-star until the surrounding water appears as a saturated solution of the same colour as the animal.

These stalkless comatulids are capable of both swimming and crawling over short distances or they can "perch" on a coral growth or the ocean bottom, holding on by means of their grasping cirri. All feed on particulate matter or small organisms from the plankton, which are trapped on a mucous slime that is conveyed towards the mouth along a system of grooves by the action of tube-feet and small beating whiplike structures called flagellae.

A small 10-armed species of feather-star occurs on reef flats, hiding beneath coral boulders. It has many colour varieties – brown, orange, green, and deep wine-red and grows to about 5 in. in diameter.

BRITTLE AND SERPENT-STARS
(Ophiuroidea)

BRITTLE-STARS have a distinct rounded body – a slightly arched disc – and five arms, which may be simple and taper towards the tip, or be branched and treelike as in the basket-stars. When foraging on a coral reef, a visitor who is not conversant with this particular group will probably be a little confused and hesitant about handling them after seeing these delicate little creatures crawling with snakelike movements of their arms over the coral rubble. By daylight they prefer the shade and seclusion beneath coral boulders and when disturbed will quickly slither away and disappear in the nearest crevice. Most are relatively small, with the disc having a diameter of between 10 to 25 mm. but this, of course, varies with the species.

The long-armed brittle-star, *Macrophiothrix longipeda*, is very common on the Reef and its arms can reach a length of approximately 12 in. When handled, most brittle-stars cast off whole arms or portions of arms and are difficult to photograph.

In the group of ophiuroids known as serpent-stars, the arms are less likely to be thrown off when they are handled and the arm spines are so reduced in size that, in some species, they appear at a first glance to be absent. A typical example of this group is the beautiful *Ophiarachna incrassata*, which is illustrated here in colour. It is mostly found on the outer edge of coral reefs beneath boulders and is very seldom, if ever, seen out in the open in daylight. This serpent-star is particularly common in the Capricorn-Bunker Groups and is probably the most spectacular of all Reef ophiuroids.

Brittle-star, *Ophiarachna incrassata* (nat. size).

BÊCHE-DE-MER
(Holothuroidea)

STREWN over exposed coral reef flats in thousands, bêche-de-mer, sometimes called trepang or sea-cucumbers, are not the most attractive of Reef fauna, but they are certainly very common in tropical and sub-tropical waters. The visitor to the area for the first time may be a little intrigued to see protruding from beneath coral boulders these black sausage-shaped holothurians and will, in most cases, be reluctant to touch such unattractive animals. But – barring a few of the rarer species – all are quite harmless and can inflict no injury whatsoever.

Some bêche-de-mer are plankton feeders, the small organisms being trapped by mucus on the

Tissue of *Chiridota rigida* examined under the microscope reveals great numbers of ossicles (x750).

surface of its tentacles (branched in the case of the genus *Holothuria*), which can be extended quite a distance from around the mouth in search of food. Others, like genus *Stichopus*, swallow great quantities of sand, from which they get their nourishment in the form of microscopic particles. As in the case of starfishes they may use tube-feet as a means of locomotion. Many species, if aggravated, will expel a mass of sticky tubules, called cuvierian organs, through the anus, and these are used purely as a defence organ against predators. Some species of bêche-de-mer throw out most of their internal organs when molested. In the case of *Holothuria leucospilota*, a large common black sea-cucumber found on all exposed coral reefs, the sticky white threads it extrudes are quite capable of immobilising large crustaceans and have amazing adhesive properties. This species is usually called the Black Cotton-spinner and may grow to about 18 in. in length.

Embedded in the body wall of bêche-de-mer are thousands of microscopic calcareous plates called ossicles which, when viewed under the microscope, are certainly unusual to observe. They are very important to the zoologist wishing to name the holothurians as they are used to determine one species from another. In the case of *Synapta maculata*, which is not like other members, the ossicles can be felt if the animal is handled. It is a member of a highly modified group (Apoda) that have no tube feet. *Synapta* can be easily recognised by its great length (it can grow to more than 6 ft.).

Key to bêche-de-mer (opposite page).
Top left—*Holothuria leucospilota*.
Top right—*Stichopus variegatus*.
Bottom — *Holothuria argus*.

Barrier Reef bêche-de-mer or sea-cucumbers.

BARRIER REEF FISHES
(Pisces)

SPECTACULAR as the surface marine life is on the Great Barrier Reef, beneath the surface is to be found a completely new world – a world that may appear a little frightening to the uninitiated, but one which is for ever throwing out a challenge and is full of mystery and beauty. No words can possibly describe this underwater wonderland – it must be seen to be appreciated. The colours and graceful movements of some of the smaller species of fishes, which teem in countless thousands in these Reef waters, are breathtaking. Such an assemblage of marine fauna is far beyond the ability of the photographer to capture. When disturbed by an inquisitive diver, many of the smaller types (demoiselles) dart for shelter amongst coral growths and, with amazing skill, dodge the razor-sharp edges of coral branches. A quick movement by the diver may be all that is necessary for these timid little creatures to disappear from sight but just as quickly, when the intruder has left, they become a little bolder and emerge from their hiding places.

One of the very common demoiselle fish is the small black-and-white *Dascyllus aruanus*, popularly known as humbugs – probably after the confection of the same colours. They are very hardy little fish and are usually associated with branching corals, *Acropora*.

The Butterfly-fishes, *Chaetodon rainfordi* and *Anisochaetodon lineolatus*, belong to a spectacular and colourful group, Chaetodontidae. Both are essentially Reef dwellers and are often found in secluded coral pools. As with humbugs, if disturbed, they will dart for shelter among the coral branches. Brilliant yellow colouring with orange crossbands and an orange-yellow spot at the tail-base makes *Chaetodon rainfordi* an outstanding little fish. It rarely exceeds 3 in. in length.

A common inhabitant of coral pools, the slow-swimming Boxfish, *Ostracion tuberculatus*, is easily recognised by its hard, bony carapace which acts as a suit of armour and protects it from predators. This northern boxfish occurs in a wide range of colours and markings, and nearly every pool on exposed coral reefs will possess one of these fascinating little creatures. The flesh is poisonous and secretes some toxic substance which quickly kills all forms of marine life if the fish is placed in an aquarium. It has no ventral fins.

The Surgeon Fish, *Teuthis*, is appropriately named, for it has a lancet-like spine on each side of the butt of the tail. This is used by the fish as a means of defence or as an aid in fighting. The species should be handled very carefully for it can inflict a nasty wound. Surgeon fishes have a wide range and are to be found throughout the Indo-Pacific.

An easily identified ray of lagoons and coral pools is the Blue-spotted Ray, *Taeniura lymna*. Its nearly oval shape and dark greyish body covered with vivid blue spots make it an outstanding member of its group. This species is very common in the Capricorn area.

A fish of rare beauty is the Firefish or Butterfly-cod, *Pterois volitans*. A slow-swimming species, its numbers have been greatly depleted on the Reef for it is very easy to catch with a scoop-net and, unfortunately, it is much in demand as an aquarium exhibit. It is a member of the Scorpion-fish group, the dorsal spines being venomous, and

The Butterfly-cod, *Pteropterus antennatus*. (x4).

has a wide distribution in tropical waters and has been seen by skindivers even in Port Jackson. The pain inflicted by the spines, if they accidentally puncture the flesh, is very severe and can last for a few months. The butterfly-cod is probably the most spectacular and beautiful of all Reef fishes. To try and describe its graceful swimming movements would be impossible, and one must really see this fish in its natural habitat to appreciate its complete contrast to other less ornate members of Reef fauna. *Pteropterus antennatus* is one of the least-known of the six species of Butterfly-cods recorded from Australian waters.

From rare beauty we move to the ugliest and most dangerous fish to be found on the Great Barrier Reef system. The Stonefish, *Synanceichthys verrucosus*, is an interesting species for it can cause death by means of venom. A few of the tribes of Australian Aborigines of Queensland made beeswax replicas of the stonefish and used them during their initiation ceremonies. During the ritual they would go through the effects of the sting, and this suggests that its presence in North Queensland waters must have been known for thousands of years. Fortunately, it is fairly rare on the Reef, but it is nearly impossible to see owing to its similarity to a clump of dead coral or eroded rock.

The adult stonefish grows to about 12 in. long and has 13 dorsal spines, each possessing two fusiform venom glands which discharge through ducts enclosed in grooves in the spines. An average of about 70 mg. of venom can be milked from an adult stonefish. The sting can be caused by treading on the fish, and the strong needle-sharp spines are capable of penetrating even a rubber boot. Fishermen have been stung in northern waters when the stonefish has been accidentally handled, after it has become mixed with other fish in a catch. If the creature is aggravated, it will instantly raise all its spines in a defensive action. Immediately after the sting, excruciating pain is felt. Rapid swelling is followed by irregular respiration, loss of blood pressure and, if a large quantity of venom has been injected, death may occur. Fortunately, an anti-venene has been developed; but in any case, the chance of anyone being stung by a stonefish while fossicking on a coral reef is practically nil.

Another species, *Synanceja trachynis*, is to be found along the Queensland coast and is very common in Moreton Bay. With this latter fish, the eyes are small and are much elevated, being carried on strong bosses. They are well separated in the case of *Synanceichthys verrucosus*, and are closer together in *Synanceja trachynis*.

A little should be explained about the giant Queensland Groper, *Promicrops lanceolatus*, for it is often encountered by divers in Reef waters. Because of its enormous mouth and head, it is certainly a fearsome cod to come in contact with and one to steer well clear of if possible. Many tales have been told about divers in the Torres Strait being swallowed whole by this bulky creature. As a general rule the species is not aggressive, but it is extremely inquisitive. Its diet mainly consists of crustaceans and other fish. It appears to frequent certain areas and, once it has chosen a cave for a home, does not wander far away from it. Each reef or coral lagoon seems to have as its guardian a pair of groper, and the writer has found this particularly noticeable in the Swain Reefs. The groper grows to about 8 ft. long and may weigh more than 650 lb., the head alone weighing at least 100 lb.

MARINE TURTLES
(Reptilia)

Turtles are reptiles and bear a relationship to lizards, snakes, and crocodiles. Their wide, flattened flippers enable them, when submerged, to swim in a most efficient manner. As air breathers, they must periodically return to the surface, and this occurs at intervals of 20 to 30 minutes, or even longer. During the egg-laying season the females must temporarily leave the sea, and this is the only link that these reptiles have with the land. While all of their kind range throughout a tropical belt around the world, they occur more prolifically in areas where coral reefs are to be found.

The most prominent and best known of the kinds which inhabit the Great Barrier Reef region is the Green Turtle, *Chelonia mydas*. This is the one that has been thoughtlessly exploited over the centuries as a source of delicate flesh, as well as for a famous soup, for human consumption. As recently as 1950 the Government in Queensland was moved to place restrictions on the taking of green turtles in Reef waters south of Latitude 13° S. (Cooktown). As a point of interest Heron Island is the only inhabited cay where turtles come ashore to lay their eggs.

The green turtle derives its name from the greenish colour of the thin, horny plates covering its bony back (carapace), and another characteristic is its relatively small head. When fully grown the species may have a carapace measuring 48 in. in length, and may weigh as much as 300 lb.

The long and tedious process that Nature has imposed on the mature female is a somewhat harrowing story. From the end of October until early in May she emerges from the sea and makes a number of nocturnal visits ashore. On an incoming tide she heaves her bulky body on to the sloping beach to begin the laborious journey over the sand to the edge of the undergrowth. Out of her natural element she appears both cumbersome and absurd, as the great body lurches forward with each determined sweep of the big front flippers. The goal is finally reached after many halts and loud sighs of exhaustion.

Soon great showers of dry sand are flung aside and backwards by the big front flippers as the female's heavy body slowly subsides into a crater-like excavation. When the stage of about body depth is reached, the stubby pair of hind flippers is employed for a special phase of the work. Using these with uncanny precision a smooth-walled shaft (egg shaft) is dug in the firmer moist sub-surface sand. The egg-laying commences slowly at first, but soon increases to about 16 eggs per minute, and once this process has begun no disturbance will distract the female from her purpose. Earlier, however, any undue noise by onlookers will cause her to cease her digging and return to the sea.

The eggs are soft and about the size of golf balls, their outer covering paperlike in appearance and rubbery to touch. They can be dropped from a height of about three feet without breaking, and can actually be bounced. About 100 eggs constitute the average clutch, but as many as 200 may be laid at a single sitting, and a female may come ashore as many as seven times during the breeding season. When an egg-laying is completed, the female brings her hind flippers into play to scoop the sand over the clutch with motherly care, gently pressing down the grains to form a final seal. The last act takes about an hour,

Overpage: Loggerhead Turtle, *Caretta caretta*, Heron Island.

for she then proceeds to camouflage the nest by throwing sand in all directions.

Thoroughly exhausted with her effort, the turtle slowly makes her way in short bursts down the incline of the beach to the water. Although her movements are pathetically clumsy while ashore, she more than makes up for this by her ability to swim at a speed of about 15 miles per hour when submerged.

The actual period the female green turtle spends on land, from the time of leaving the sea until the movement of re-entry, is between two and three hours. It has been estimated that, in the excavation of the initial crater in the egg-laying process, a female will displace almost a ton of sand.

The eggs, left deserted by the female, lie deep and snug in the sand and incubate over a period of from six to 10 weeks. The developing embryos are sustained meantime by a liberal supply of yolk which is not entirely absorbed by the emerging young until about a couple of days after hatching. It is only then that they laboriously force themselves upwards to the surface, and immediately make their way to the sea. Extraordinarily enough, the hatchlings are so sensitive to light that they will even blunder into an open fire. If migration to the sea takes place at night, a big percentage of the hatchlings will safely reach the water. Some will fall victim to the nocturnal Ghost Crab, *Ocypode ceratophthalma*, which will kill as though in some ecstatic mood of destruction. During daylight the ravenous seagulls swoop upon the hatchlings and quickly deplete their numbers. Even after reaching the apparent safety of the sea great numbers of them become prey for predatory fish.

It is thus in this seemingly cruel way that a balance of Nature is preserved, so that only about 4 per cent of green turtles will survive to reach maturity. Added to all these dangers is an unsuspected attack made on the eggs during the incubation period. While making a study of embryo stages, the writer has found many of them to be non-fertile. Examination of the contents under the microscope disclosed that these had been destroyed by parasitic thread-worms (nematodes), which were present in great numbers.

Only sparse knowledge has been gained about the earliest growing stages of the green turtles in the sea. Fishermen fail to capture any of the very young in their nets, and not even a sighting by the numerous skindivers who operate in Reef waters is known to the writer. A solitary case that has come under notice was the capture by fishermen of a 12-in. long juvenile green turtle brought to the surface from deep water in a mass of seaweed. Under controlled conditions some valuable data on growth are being obtained by an enthusiastic naturalist of Brisbane, L. Tanis, who has been raising and studying turtles in aquaria for many years. In particular, he has had outstanding success with a female albino green turtle brought as a hatchling from Heron Island. In four years it has increased in weight from an initial $\frac{3}{4}$ oz. to 43 lb.

At any place along the Reef where green turtles are found, the ugly Loggerhead Turtle, *Caretta caretta*, will also be seen. It has a large head, with a strong and pointed overhanging upper jaw, capable of giving a vicious bite. The general colour is predominantly brownish and, where exposed, the skin varies between brown and a yellowish-orange shade. The maximum length of

Overpage: Male Green Turtle, *Chelonia mydas*, Broomfield Reef, Capricorn Group.

the completely bony shell or carapace is approximately 42 in. – a little less than that of the green turtle. When crossing over land the loggerhead has somewhat of a walking action, far more easily performed than the dragging movement of the green turtle; the eggs, too, are smaller and of a faint pinkish hue. On rare occasions the females leave the sea to lay their eggs during daylight. Upon completion of an egg-laying, a noticeable variation from the behaviour of female green turtles is that the loggerhead spares only about 20 minutes in disguising her nest. Because of the reputation for aggression this same ugly turtle has earned, it is treated with some respect and, when in the sea, is given a wide berth by skindivers. Eye-witness reports by the latter tell of loggerhead turtles attacking schools of fish with skill and remarkable agility. While the normal diet is one of flesh, it has been asserted that the loggerhead can be an omnivorous feeder.

A kind of turtle that is far less frequently seen in Reef waters than either of the two preceding ones is the Hawk's-bill Turtle, *Eretmochelys imbricata*. It has a more flattened body, a curved, very beaklike upper jaw, and is easily recognised by its covering of prettily marked, thick, horny, brown and yellow overlapping plates. This is the particular turtle which has for centuries been the source of so-called "tortoise-shell". In the northern section of the Reef the female hawk's-bill is known occasionally to come ashore to lay her eggs. Of purely carnivorous habit, this turtle can hunt and capture fish with great skill.

Another turtle occurring in Reef waters is *Dermochelys coriacea*, which is quite a rarity, and a veritable giant among its kind. Its name of Luth or Leatherback Turtle has been aptly applied, for the tough integument of its carapace possesses no covering of horny plates. It is mainly an inhabitant of deeper water and ranges far and wide over the oceans; unlike other turtles, it commonly penetrates into temperate zones such as the coastal waters of New South Wales. Although few are ever captured, it is known that the leatherback may grow to a length of 9 ft. 6 in. and weigh as much as 1 ton. Breeding apparently takes place only in the tropics, and two areas selected for this near the Australian region are the Solomon Islands and Malaya.

Mention should be made of male turtles. As these never leave their native element, it stands to reason that far more knowledge of an interesting nature has been accumulated about the opposite sex. Males are always smaller in size than females and hence more active. This is particularly noticeable with the male green turtle, which possesses a long tail and has been closely observed by the writer during many a breeding season.

A fact not generally known is that another turtle does occur in far northern Australian coastal waters. It is the Flatback or Greyback Turtle, *Chelonia depressa* and tends to have a carapace which is flatter and considerably lighter in colour than the common green turtle. Rarely seen, it grows to about the same size as the latter turtle and the female flatback lays her eggs on coastal and island beaches.

SEA-SNAKES
(Reptilia)

ALTHOUGH PLENTIFUL in Great Barrier Reef waters, these venomous marine reptiles are only occasionally seen swimming or basking in the sun on the surface of the water in both coral lagoons and deep water. They are true reptiles and are characterised by scales and a paddle-shaped tail, using this to propel themselves through the water at a speed equivalent to that of any fast-swimming fish. Possessing lungs, they must surface to breathe. They are capable of staying submerged for long periods, certain species for at least 30 minutes, before surfacing to replenish their air supply. Sea-snakes (Hydrophiidae) all have small flaps of skin which act as valves to seal the nostrils when submerged.

Many people who visit northern waters confuse reef eels with sea-snakes and a rather false impression may be gained of the number of true sea-snakes which occur in the Reef region. Eels are true fish and are not related in any way to these reptiles. The first impression one would gain when seeing an eel swimming or darting amongst coral growths would be that it is a sea-snake. An eel such as *Echidna nebulosa*, whose thick black-and-white banded body and quick movements in the water resemble those of a sea-snake in every way, is easy to mistake for a reptile.

Sea-snakes often seem to congregate in certain areas. For instance, they are prevalent in coastal harbours such as Port Curtis, Gladstone, and can be quite a nuisance to fishermen there. In fact, reliable reports from skindivers working in this particular area indicate that sea-snakes from these Queensland coastal waters can be quite aggressive. Then, as one proceeds seawards,

concentrations sometimes occur at the Swain Reefs and Kenn Reefs. Great numbers have been seen at the Chesterfield Reefs and Wreck Reefs, which appear to be breeding grounds for sea-snakes. In between these locations they are very rarely seen.

Just how dangerous are sea-snakes? This has been asked many times by visitors who have seen one for the first time. It has been found that in many cases the reptile's venom is more potent than that of many of the world's most deadly land snakes. Fortunately, all sea-snakes have very small fangs and consequently only a little venom is injected at one bite. This, combined with the fact that these reptiles are not normally aggressive, is the reason why no fatalities have so far occurred in Great Barrier Reef waters.

Many reports have been given, especially over the last few years, by spear-fishermen and skin-divers who have claimed that they have been attacked in force by great numbers while diving in Reef waters. In some of these highly coloured accounts, they barely escaped with their lives. If molested by humans, sea-snakes will naturally become annoyed and attempt to defend themselves, but the writer has not found them aggressive in any way – possibly a little inquisitive – but, if left alone, they will in most cases swim away from the diver.

There are about two dozen species which occur in Reef waters. One of these, *Pelamis platurus*, which also is to be found in southern waters, is easily recognised by the bright yellow underside of its body. Deaths have been recorded from waters around Malaya, where the species occurs quite abundantly. Its average length is about 30 in. and a specimen 44 in. long was found in the lagoon at Lord Howe Island.

The large Sea-snake, *Astrotia stokesii*.

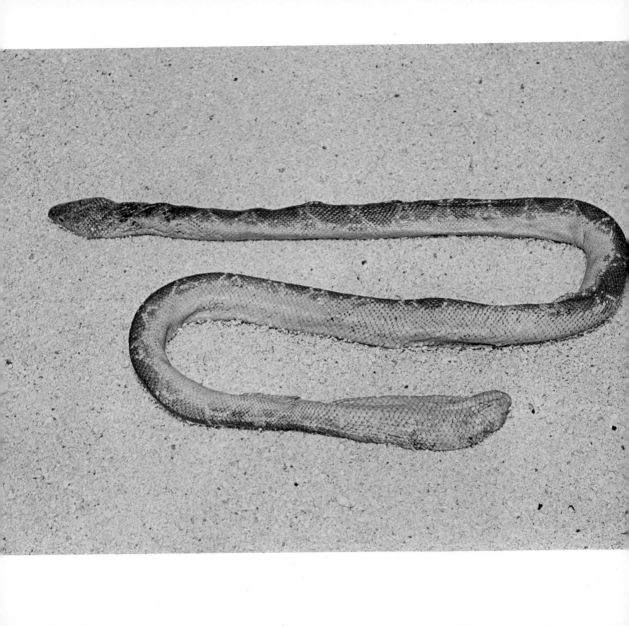

SOME BIRDS OF THE CAPRICORN-BUNKER GROUPS AND CORAL SEA

To give a detailed account of all the land and seabirds which inhabit the Reef system would be an impossible task in a book such as this. A few of the more commonly seen species have been chosen, for any book written about the region must make mention of the fascinating birds which frequent the area. It has been stated that "the coral cays of the Reef are a magnet for the birds of the Pacific". During the summer breeding season this is quite true of these little coral specks which, because of their isolation, are ideal breeding grounds for birds. It is a memorable experience to visit the area at this time of the year. Civilisation seems to be a thing apart and soon the visitor has forgotten the bustling city life and is transported in spirit back to a period when animal life lived without interference from humanity.

An avian visitor, and one which arrives in countless thousands, is the Wedge-tailed Shearwater or Muttonbird, *Puffinus pacificus*. Many of the cays in the Capricorn-Bunker Groups are honeycombed with the long burrows of these birds. It is almost impossible, when walking through the undergrowth, not to crash through to their nesting places. At North West Island, it is even a little dangerous to explore the inner part of the cay because almost every square yard of the loose coral sand covers an underground nest. In 1925 it was estimated that at least 2,000,000 shearwaters occupied North West Island in the breeding season.

During the day the shearwaters are not active ashore. Those not brooding fly out to sea in search of small fish such as hardyheads. At sunset, or a little earlier, they come in to land and soon the air is filled with their weird, mournful cries, at first low in volume and then gradually building up in a crescendo. To be at sea and hear such a wailing is a mystifying experience, especially when the sounds may be caused by a million or more birds.

The shearwater skims low over the sea and is a very graceful bird in flight. It grows to a length of about 14 in. and its dark brownish bill is long and hooked. Strange as it may seem, these birds are very clumsy on land and remind one of an aeroplane about to become airborne. At dawn, it is an amazing sight to see them slowly building up speed by running on their short and poorly developed legs down apparently recognised runways between the trees before finally taking to the air. Once they are airborne it is quite a different story, for they are strong fliers and are capable of travelling great distances.

The Greater Frigate Bird, *Fregata minor*, and the Lesser Frigate Bird, *Fregata ariel*, noted for their great wing-span (up to 7 ft.), have a body length of approximately 3 ft. and a weight of some 3 lb. They are usually seen hovering over coral cays, and their presence is sometimes followed by bad weather. Consequently, local fishermen do not welcome them. They have been referred to as "thieves of the sky" for they seem to delight in stealing food from terns, gannets, and other seabirds. This they do by making their victim disgorge their food which they then expertly catch in mid-air. Very little is known about their main breeding grounds, but thousands of these birds nest on the numerous

Masked Gannet, *Sula dactylatra*, Swain Reefs.

small cays which are associated with the Chesterfield Reefs, some 600 miles NE of Port Curtis, Queensland. Their nests are composed of sticks and grass, and are built either on the ground or in shrubs and small trees.

Gannets and boobies are particularly tame and are easy to photograph. The Brown Gannet, *Sula leucogaster*, is to be found in small colonies on Fairfax Island and Lady Musgrave Island. The Masked Gannet, *Sula dactylatra*, and the Red-footed Gannet, *Sula sula*, breed on the coral cays. The masked gannet does not make a nest; a mere scrape or depression in the coral sand holds the two eggs. The other two species build nests, that of the red-footed gannet being rather substantial and generally in trees. All gannets can be approached quite easily and seem to have little fear of human beings. The word booby is derived from *bobo*, a term used by early mariners for the various species. The meaning of this Spanish or Portuguese word is "fool". It seems that these relatively large birds, which vary in weight from 2 to 5 lb., were caught without any trouble by early voyagers.

The Crested Tern, *Sterna bergii*, is distinguished by a lemon-yellow beak, a white body, and a black crown. Masthead Island is a favourite nesting place of this species, whose eggs are laid on the sand or grass in a scrape or a scanty nest. The Black-naped Tern, *Sterna sumatrana*, easily identified by a black patch running from eye to nape, is also a ground nester and makes a depression in the coral sand just above high-water mark. It is often associated with the Roseate Tern, *Sterna dougallii*, which also occurs in scattered colonies in the area. The latter bird is one of the loveliest to be found in the region. Growing to about 14 in. in length, its forehead,

crown and nape are black and the remainder of its body is greyish and white with a pale pinkish tinge. One of the darker-coloured terns, the Sooty Tern, *Sterna fuscata*, nests in great colonies on Reef cays.

The Common Noddy, *Anous stolidus*, with its chocolate-brown body and pale grey cap, is the largest of the two species of noddies found in the Coral Sea region. It prefers to breed in large colonies on the ground though it also nests in shrubs and trees. The second species, the White-capped Noddy, *Anous minutus*, is smaller, daintier, and darker in plumage and is numerous in the Capricorn-Bunker Groups. It usually makes its nest (seaweed and leaves) in trees.

It may seem a little out of the ordinary when one is out examining an exposed coral reef to see either a dark greyish or a pure white, long-legged, long-beaked bird, fossicking among the coral. This explorer is the Reef Heron, *Demigretta sacra*, which has a very wide distribution along the coasts of Australia, Tasmania, India, and Japan. It prefers the tops of pandanus or tournefortia trees in which to nest and is a shy bird.

The largest and most powerful landbird in the Capricorn-Bunker Groups is the White-breasted Sea-eagle, *Haliaetus leucogaster*. It is interesting to note that on 12 August, 1770 the naturalists Banks and Solander on board the *Endeavour*, landed on a small islet near the northern end of the Reef. Here they found the nest of a sea-eagle containing young birds. Because of these circumstances, Captain Cook named the place Eagle Islet.

One of the smaller landbirds but one which is quite common on Heron Island is the Bar-shouldered Dove, *Geopelia humeralis*. It makes its stick nest in the tops of trees.

White-capped Noddy and nestling, *Anous minutus*, Heron Island.

INDEX

Light figures indicate main text references
Bold figures indicate Black and White or Colour Plates

Abrolhos Islands, 8
Acanthaster planci, 72, **73**
Acanthozostera gemmata, 20, 44
Acrhelia horrescens, 16
Acropora humilis, 16, **19**
Actinia tenebrosa, 34
Actiniaria, 14, 32 to 37, **33**
Actinodendron plumosum, 36
Aglaophenia cupressina, 30, **30**
Alcyonaria, 22 to 25, **23**, **24**, **25**, **27**
Amphiprion melanopus, 34, **35**
Anemone fish, 34, **35**
Anisochaetodon lineolatus, 80
Anous minutus, 92, **93**
Aristotle's Lantern (Echinoidea), 74
Astrotia stokesii, 88, **89**
Atoll, 8, 10

Bar-shouldered Dove, 92
Baseodiscus quinquelineatus, 38
Baseodiscus sp. 40, **40**
Beche-de-mer (Holothuroidea), 78, **78**, **79**
Birds, 90, 92, **91**, **93**
Bivalves (Pelecypoda), 44, 56, 58, **56**, **57**, **58**, **59**
   Amusium balloti, 56, **57**
   Fragum unedo, 56, **57**
   Gloripallium pallium, 56, **57**
   Hippopus hippopus, 58, **58**
   Laciolina quoyi, 56, **57**
   Lentillaria paytenorum, 56, **57**
   Lioconcha castrensis, 56, **57**
   Promantellum parafragile, 56, **56**
   Regozara flava, 56, **57**
   Scutarcopagia linguafelis, 56, **57**
   Solen aureomaculatus, 56, **57**
   Tapes literata, 56, **57**
   Tridacna crocea, 58
   Tridacna gigas, 58
   Tridacna maxima, 58, **59**
   Trisidos yongei, 56, **57**
Black Cotton-spinner, 78
Black-naped Tern, 92
Blue-spotted Ray, 80
Boxfish, 80
Brain Coral, 14, 16, **15**
Bristle Worm, 38, 40, 42, **42**
Brittle and Serpent-stars (Ophiuroidea), 76, **77**

Broomfield Reef, 18, 72
Butterfly-cod, 80, 82, **81**
Butterfly-fishes, 80

Calliactis polypus, 36, 64
Capricorn-Bunker Groups, 4, 10, 12, 16, 18, 26, 58, 72, 76, 80, 92, **7**, **9**
Carols's Volute, 48, **47**
Carophyllia, 6
Carpilius maculatus, 66
Cephalopoda, 44, 62, **63**
Chaetodontidae, 80
Chaetodon rainfordi, 80
Charonia, with ref to Crown of Thorns, 72
Chelonia depressa, 87
Chelonia mydas, 83, 85, **86**
Chesterfield Reefs, 10, 12, 72, 88, 92
Chiridota rigida, 78, **77**
Chitons, 20, 44
Chromodoris quadricolor, 60
Clams (Tridacnidae), 44, 58, **58**
Clibanarius virescens, 64
Cnidaria, 14 to 36, **15 to 37**
Coelenterata, 14 to 36, **15 to 37**
Coenobita perlatus, 64, 66, **67**
Coenobita rugosa, 64, 66
Commensalism, 34, **35**
Cone Shells, 44, 50, **50**, **51**, **52**, **53**
   Conus (Chelyconus) catus, 52, **53**
   Conus (Cleobula) figulina, 52, **53**
   Conus (Cylinder) textile, 50, 52, **53**
   Conus (Gastridiuim) geographus, 50, 52, **53**
   Conus (Pionoconus) suturatus, 50, **53**
   Conus (Regiconus) aulicus, 52, **53**
   Conus (Rhizoconus) miles, 52, **53**
   Conus (Rhizoconus) vexillum, 52, **53**
   Conus (Rhombus) imperialis, 52, **53**
   Conus (Strioconus) striatus, 50, 52, **50**, **51**, **53**
   Conus (Tuliparia) tulipa, 50, 52, **53**
   Conus (Virroconus) imperator, 50, **53**
Cowry Shells, 22, 26, 44, 46, **45**, **47**
   Calpurnus verrucosus, 46, **47**
   Cypraea annulus, 46, **47**
   Cypraea argus, 46, **47**
   Cypraea asellus, 46, **47**
   Cypraea carneola, 46, **47**
   Cypraea cribraria, 44, 46, **45**, **47**

Cypraea eburnea, 46, **47**
Cypraea erosa, 46, **47**
Cypraea facifer, 46, **47**
Cypraea helvolva, 46, **47**
Cypraea isabella, 46, **47**
Cypraea moneta, 46, **47**
Cypraea staphylaea, 46, **47**
Cypraea tigris, 46, **46**, **47**
Cypraea vitellus, 46, **47**
Ovula ovum, 22, 46, **47**
Volva volva, 46, **47**
Crabs, 64, 66, 68, **65**, **67**, **69**
Crayfish, 68
Crown of Thorns Starfish, 72, **73**
Crustacea, 64 to 68, **65 to 69**

Dandanus deformis, 64
Dardanus megistos, 64, 68, **69**
Darwin, Charles, 4, 8, 10
Dascyllus aruanus, 80
Demigretta sacra, 92
Dermochelys coriacea, 87
Diadema setosum, 72, 74

Echidna nebulosa, 88
Echinoderms, 70 to 78, **71 to 79**
Echinoidea, 74, **75**
Echinometra mathaei, 74
Eriphia sebana, 64, 66, **65**
Eurythoe complanata, 38, 40, 42, **42**

Feather-stars (Crinoidea), 76
Fiji Islands, 4, 12
Fishes, 80, 82, **81**
Flatworms, 32, 38, 87, **39**
Foraminifera, 8
Frigate Birds, 90, 92
Fungia actiniformis, 18, **21**
Fungia fungites, 18

Gannets, 92, **93**
Galathea elegans, 26, **26**
Geopelia humeralis, 92
Ghost Crabs, 64, 66, 85, **65**
Goniopora tenuidens, 14, 16, **17**
Gorgonacea, 26, **27**
Gall Crab, 66
Greater Frigate Bird, 90, 92
Green Turtle, 83, 85, 87, **86**
Gymnodoris ceylonica, 60, **61**

Haliaetus leucogaster, 92
Hapalocarcinus marsupialis, 66
Hapalochlaena lunulatus, 74
Hapalochlaena maculosa, 62

Hawk's-bill Turtle, 87
Heliopora coerulea, 24
Hermit Crabs, 64, 66, 68, **67**, **69**
Heron Island, 4, 12, 20, 62, 83, 85, 92, **9**, **13**
Herpolitha limax, 18
Hexabranchus imperialis, 60
Hippopus hippopus, 58, **58**
Holothuria argus, 78, **79**
Holothuria leucospilota, 78, **79**
Horse-hoof Clam, 58, **57**
Hydrophiidae, 88, **89**
Hydrozoa, 28, 30, **28**, **29**, **30**, **31**

Kenn Reefs, 12, 88
Kent, Saville, 5, 20, 24, 36

Lambis lambis, 54
Lesser Frigate Bird, 90, 92
Lima, 56, **56**
Linckia laevigata, 70, 72
Linckia guildingii, 72
Linderman Island, 8
Lithothamnion, 6
Lobophyton, 22
Loggerhead Turtle, 83, 85, 87, **84**
Low Isles, 12, 74
Lytocarpus philippinus, 30, **31**
Lytocarpus pheoniceus, 30

Macrophiothrix longipeda, 76
Masked Gannet, 92, **93**
Millepora platyphylla, 30, **29**
Mollusca, 26, 44 to 62, **45 to 63**
Montipora, 16
Mopsella ellisi, 26, **27**

Nardoa novaecaledoniae, 70, 72, **71**
Nardoa pauciforis, 72
Nematocysts, 28, 32, 36, **28**
Nemerteans, 38, 40, **39**
New Caledonia, 4, 6, 52, 72
Nivigena melwardi, 44, **45**
Nudibranchs (Nudibranchia), 32, 60, **61**

Octopus, 44, 62, **63**
Ocypode ceratophthalma, 64, 66, 85, **65**
Ocypode cordimana, 66
One Tree Island, 12, 18, 72
Ophiarachna incrassata, 76, **77**
Organ-pipe Coral, 24, **23**
Ostracion tuberculatus, 80
Ovula ovum, 22, 46, **47**

Palythoa caesia, 34, 46, **47**
Panulirus longipes, 68
Panulirus ornatus, 68

Panulirus versicolor, 68
Pelamis platurus, 88
Photosynthesis, 6
Physobrachia ramsayi, 34, **35**
Planulae, 16, 18
Pocillipora, 16
Polycladida, **38**, **39**
Polyphyllia, 18
Porites, 16, 20
Promicrops lanceolatus, 40
Pseudoceros bedfordi, 38, **39**
Pseudoceros corallophilus, 38
Pterois volitans, 80
Pteropterus antennatus, 80, 82, **81**
Puffinus pacificus, 90

Ranina ranina, 64, 68, **65**
Reef Heron, 92
Reteterebella queenslandia, 42, **43**
Rhodactis howesi, 36, **37**
Roseate Tern, 92

Sabellastarte indica, 40, **41**
Sarcophyton trocheliophorum, 22, **23**
Saumarez Reef, 12, 72
Scaphopoda, 44
Scleratcinia, 14 to 20, **15 to 21**
Scorpion Fish, 80, **81**
Sea anemones, 14, 32 to 36, **33 to 37**
Sea-cucumbers, 4, 78, **79**
Sea-eagle, 92
Sea-snakes, 62, 88, **89**
Sea-urchins, 74, **75**
Sinularia, 22
Soft Corals, 22, 26, **23 to 27**
Sooty Tern, 92
Spanner Crab, 64, 66, 68, **65**
Spirobranchus giganteus, 20
Starfishes (Asteroidea), 70, 72, **71**, **73**
Stenopus hispidus, 68
Sterna bergii, 92
Sterna dougallii, 92
Sterna fuscata, 92
Stichopus variegatus, 78, **79**
Stinging Corals, 28, 30, **28 to 31**
Stoichactis haddoni, 34, **33**

Stoichactis kenti, 34
Stonefish, 82
Strombs (Strombidae), 44, 54, **53**, **55**
   Strombus (Conomurex) luhuanus, 54, **53**, **55**
   Strombus (Dolomena) variabilis, 54, **55**
   Strombus (Doxander) vittatus, 54, **55**
   Strombus (Euprotomus) aratrum, 54, **55**
   Strombus (Gibberulus) gibberulus, 54, **55**
   Strombus (Laevistrombus) canarium, 54, **55**
   Strombus (Lentigo) lentiginosus, 54, **55**
Sula dactylatra, 92, 93
Sula leucogaster, 92
Sula sula, 92
Swain Reefs, 4, 10, 82, 88
Synanceja trachynis, 82
Synanceichthys verrucosus, 82
Synapta maculata, 78

Teuthis, 80
Thalamita stimpsoni, 66
Tridacna crocea, 58
Tridacna gigas, 58
Tridacna maxima, 58
Tubipora musica, 24
Turtles, 5, 83 to 87, **84**, **85**

Ultra-violet irradiation, 36

Vermes, 38, 40, 42, **39**, **41**, **43**
Volutes (Volutidae), 44, 48, **47**, **49**
   Amoria maculata, 48, **47**, **49**
   Aulicina sophiae, 48, **49**
   Cymbiolacca complexa, 48, **49**
   Cymbiolacca cracenta, 48, **49**
   Cymbiolacca pulchra, 48, **49**
   Cymbiolacca wisemani, 48, **49**
   Cymbiolacca wisemani, (randalli form), 48, **49**
   Volutoconus grossi, 48, **49**

Wedge-tailed Shearwater, 90
Western Samoa, 4, 12, 52, 66, 72
White-capped Noddy, 92, **93**
Worms, 38 to 42, **39 to 43**
Wreck Reefs, 4, 12, 88

Xenia elongata, 22, **25**

Zooxanthellae, 6